Shakespe

HAMLET

*A shortened version
in modern English*

by
John and Leela Hort

≈ KP̃ ≈

THE KABET PRESS

Copyright © 1999 John & Leela Hort
First published 1999 by The Kabet Press

By the same authors
HENRY V
TWELFTH NIGHT
ROMEO AND JULIET
A MIDSUMMER NIGHT'S DREAM
MACBETH

Permission must be obtained and a fee paid before this play is
performed in public, whether or not there is an admission fee.
Details can be obtained from:

www.schoolplayproductions.co.uk
SchoolPlay Productions Ltd
15 Inglis Road
Colchester
N CO6 3BN
01206 540111
NB It is illegal to copy this play in whole or in part
by any reproductive process.

A CIP catalogue record for this book
is available from the British Library.

ISBN 0 948662 05 0

Designed and typeset
using community DTP resources at
CODA Nottingham

Printed by The Russell Press Ltd,
Russell House, Bulwell Lane, Basford,
Nottingham NG6 0BT

CONTENTS

The Scene is Denmark
and most of the play takes place in
the Royal Castle at Elsinore

PEOPLE IN THE PLAY

Ghost	The ghost of the late King Hamlet
King	Claudius, King of Denmark, brother of the late King
Queen	Gertrude, Queen of Denmark, widow of the late King
Hamlet	A prince. Son of the late King Hamlet and Queen Gertrude
Polonius	The King's chief adviser
Laertes	Polonius' son
Ophelia	Polonius' daughter
Reynaldo	Servant to Polonius
Horatio	A good friend of Hamlet

Rosencrantz⎫ Childhood friends of Hamlet,
Guildenstern⎭ and members of the Danish court

Cornelius⎫ Danish councillors and
Voltemand⎭ ambassadors to Norway

Osric A wealthy Danish landowner

A Lord⎫ Members of the
A Gentleman⎭ Danish Court

Francisco⎫
Bernardo⎬ Danish soldiers, members of the King's Guard
Marcellus⎭

Fortinbras	Prince of Norway
Captain	An officer in the Norwegian army
English Ambassadors	
Actors	In the play in Act 3 Scene 1, one actor plays the **King**, another the **Queen**, a third is **Lucianus**, and a fourth speaks the **Prologue**

Two Gravediggers
A Priest
A Sailor

Non-speaking parts: **Attendants, Messengers, Musicians, Sailors, Danish Soldiers, Norwegian Soldiers**

> The names of the characters in each scene are given in a box at the beginning of the scene. (Non-speaking parts are in brackets.)

ACT ONE

Scene 1
Elsinore, the castle wall

Francisco
Bernardo
Horatio
Marcellus
(Ghost)

[*It is midnight.* **Francisco** *is on guard, and* **Bernardo** *is coming to take over from him*]

Bernardo Who's there?

Francisco No, tell me who *you* are!

Bernardo [*Coming in*] Long live the King!

Francisco Bernardo! You're very punctual.

Bernardo It's after twelve. Get to bed, Francisco.

Francisco Thanks. [*He shivers*] Brr, it's cold—and I'm miserable!

Bernardo Has it been quiet?

Francisco As a mouse!

Bernardo Well, good night! If you see Horatio and Marcellus, tell them to hurry.

Francisco I think I can hear them. [*He calls out*] Who's there?

[**Horatio** *and* **Marcellus** *come in as* **Bernardo** *moves away along the wall*]

Horatio Friends.

Marcellus And loyal Danes.

Francisco [*Moving off*] Good night!

Marcellus Good night, my friend. Who's taken over?

Francisco Bernardo. Good night! [*He goes out*]

1

Bernardo [*Coming back*] Is Horatio there?

Horatio [*Yawning*] A bit of him!

Bernardo Welcome, Horatio. Hello, Marcellus!

Horatio [*To Bernardo*] Well, has this thing appeared again?

Bernardo I haven't seen anything.

Marcellus [*To Bernardo*] Horatio says we're imagining it, even though we've seen it twice.

Horatio Nonsense! It won't appear!

Bernardo Sit down. We'll have another try at convincing you.

Horatio [*To Marcellus*] All right, let's listen to what Bernardo has to say. [*They all sit down*]

Bernardo Well, last night, at exactly this time, Marcellus and I—

Marcellus Sh! Here it comes again.

[*The **Ghost** of Hamlet's father comes in, dressed in armour*]

Bernardo [*Whispering*] It looks just like the dead King.

Marcellus [*Whispering*] You'll know what to say, Horatio. You speak to it!

Bernardo [*To Horatio*] Don't you think it looks like the King?

Horatio [*Slowly*] Yes... It's uncanny...

Bernardo It's waiting to be spoken to.

Marcellus Go on, Horatio.

Horatio [*To the Ghost*] What are you? What are you doing here? At this hour—in armour, like our dead King! [*Pause*] Answer me!

Marcellus It's offended.

Bernardo It's moving away.

Horatio Stop! Speak! I order you to speak! [*The **Ghost** goes out*]

Bernardo Horatio, you're frightened! Well, was that just our imagination?

Horatio I would never have believed it if I hadn't seen it with my own eyes!

Marcellus Wasn't it like the King?

Horatio Exactly. The same armour, the same angry frown. It's strange... I fear it means trouble for Denmark.

Marcellus Come, sit down. [*They sit down again*] Now, can either of you tell me why we are having to keep guard, and why our people are being forced to work day and night, making guns, importing weapons and building ships? What's going on? Why all this sweat and toil?

Horatio I think I can explain. As you probably know, the King whose ghost we have just seen was once challenged to a duel by proud old Fortinbras of Norway. Fortinbras was killed, and his estates were made over to King Hamlet, as a result of a wager the two men had made. But now *young* Fortinbras, old Fortinbras' hot-blooded son, has got together a band of ruffians and is determined to fight to recover the land that his father lost. Hence these frantic preparations and this guard.

Bernardo I'm sure you're right. And that would explain why this ominous figure has appeared, dressed in armour, and looking so like the King who caused the conflict in the first place.

Horatio Eclipses, comets trailing fire, the dead walking in the streets—all these have acted as warnings in the past, and even in our own times... Look! Here it comes again. [*The **Ghost** comes in again*] I'll risk damnation! [*He goes up to it*] Speak to me, if you have a voice! [*He waits*] Can I help you in some way? [*He waits*] Can you see into the future? Have you come to warn your country? [*He waits*] Is there something you need to do here on earth? [*The **Ghost** is about to speak but a cock crows and it moves away*] Try and stop it, Marcellus!

Marcellus [*Grabbing his spear*] Shall I use this?

Horatio Yes, if it won't stop. [*They try to attack the **Ghost***]

Bernardo Here it is!

Horatio It's over here! [*The **Ghost** vanishes*]

Marcellus It's gone! We shouldn't have attacked it. It looked so dignified. Besides, it's ridiculous to get so worked up about thin air!

Bernardo It was about to speak when the cock crowed.

Horatio Then it started and looked guilty. They say the cock crowing at dawn is a warning to wandering spirits to hurry back to their graves. Here's proof of it.

Marcellus They also say that at Christmas time the cock crows all night long, to prevent ghosts and witches from doing harm.

Horatio I've heard that too, and I'm half inclined to believe it... But look, dawn is breaking. We can go off duty now. I think we ought to tell young Hamlet what we've seen tonight. The ghost won't speak to us, but I'm sure it will speak to him. Do you agree?

Marcellus Yes, and I know where we can find him this morning.

King	Hamlet
Queen	(Lords)
Cornelius	(Attendants)
Voltemand	Horatio
Laertes	Bernardo
Polonius	Marcellus

Scene 2
A State apartment in the castle

[*King Claudius* and *Queen Gertrude* come in with *Hamlet*, *Polonius*, *Laertes*, *Cornelius*, *Voltemand*, *Lords* and *Attendants*]

King [*Addressing the Court*] Although the memory of our dear brother Hamlet's death is fresh in our minds, and it is natural that we and our whole kingdom should mourn for him, nevertheless I have now managed to overcome my feelings sufficiently to consider my own affairs. So it is with both joy and sorrow that I have made my former sister-in-law—our Queen—my wife. Thank you all for your excellent advice, and for your generous support. [*Applause*] What follows, you know already. Young Fortinbras, thinking that our brother's death has left us weak and disorganised, and hoping to take advantage, keeps pestering us to give up the lands which his father forfeited to my brother. So much for him. Now, I have written to his uncle, the King of Norway, who is bedridden and hardly knows what his nephew is doing, asking him to intervene, since it is *his* army that is being used. Cornelius and Voltemand, you will take this message to the Norwegian King, and negotiate within the guidelines set out here. [*He gives them some papers*] Now go! You must act quickly.

Cornelius & **Voltemand** We will, your Majesty. [*They go out*]

King Now, Laertes. What about you? You mentioned some business. What is it, Laertes? I am prepared to allow any reasonable request. You only have to ask. Your father could not be more dear to the King of Denmark. What is it you want, Laertes?

Laertes My lord, your gracious permission to return to France. I was happy to attend your coronation, but now that I have done my duty I would like to return, if I may.

King Have you your father's permission? What does Polonius say?

Polonius My lord, he has obtained my grudging consent. Please let him go.

King Then enjoy your youth, Laertes, and use your talents well. [*Turning to Hamlet*] Now Hamlet, my nephew, my son—

Hamlet [*To himself*] —too close for comfort!—

King —still clouded with sadness?

Hamlet No, my lord. I'm too much in the sun.

Queen Dear Hamlet, don't be so miserable. Try to see the King as a friend. You can't go on mourning your noble father's death for ever. You know that death is our common fate, that all who live must die.

Hamlet Yes, madam, it is common.

Queen Then why make it seem so special?

Hamlet Seem, madam? No, it *is*. These dark clothes, this sad face, the sighing and the crying, these are what *seem*. A man can put them on. Real sorrow lies within.

King Of course it is right and proper for you to mourn for your father, Hamlet. But remember, your father lost a father, and he lost his, and each of them was duty bound to mourn for a certain time. But to go on and on shows a kind of disrespect, an unwillingness to submit to God's will; it is not manly, it betrays a lack of courage, of patience. It's almost simple-minded. Something so inevitable, so commonplace, why take it so to heart? Shame on you! It's an insult to heaven, an offence against the dead, against nature, against reason. Abandon this pointless grief, and look upon me as a father. I hereby proclaim you my heir, and extend to you a father's deepest love! As for your wish to return to college at Wittenburg, I am opposed to it, and I urge you to accept our hospitality and remain here as our son.

Queen Answer your mother's prayer, Hamlet. Please stay with us. Don't go to Wittenburg!

Hamlet I will do my best to obey you, madam.

King A good and loving reply! Yes, stay with us here. [*To the **Queen***] Come, madam. I'm delighted that Hamlet has agreed so willingly. Tonight, every time I drink a toast, the guns shall fire in celebration. Come!

[*They all go out except **Hamlet***]

Hamlet [*To himself*] Oh, if only this foul body of mine would just melt away! Or that the Almighty hadn't forbidden us to take our own lives! God! God! how tedious, how pointless the world seems. Ugh! It's like a garden choked with weeds... That it should come to this! Just two months dead—no, less than that. And such a fine king—a god compared to this beast! And so loving to my mother, so gentle, so kind... Oh heavens! must I remember? She couldn't have enough of him, and yet within a month... I can't bear to think of it. Weakness, your name is woman! One little month... Before the shoes in which she went weeping to my poor father's grave were worn out, she—oh, God! an *animal* would have mourned longer—married my uncle, my father's brother; but no more like my father than I am like Hercules! What foul wickedness, to rush into an incestuous bed. No good can come of it. But my heart will break, for I must hold my tongue.

[**Horatio, Marcellus** and **Bernardo** *come in*]

Horatio Good morning, your lordship.

Hamlet [*Preoccupied*] Good morning. [*He realises who it is*] Horatio— unless I'm mistaken.

Horatio Yes, my lord. Your humble servant.

Hamlet My *friend!* We can call each other friend! And what brings you from Wittenburg, Horatio? [*To* **Marcellus**] Good morning, Marcellus.

Marcellus My lord—

Hamlet I'm very glad to see you. [*To* **Bernardo**] Good morning, sir. [*To* **Horatio**] But what are you doing here?

Horatio I'm playing truant.

Hamlet Nonsense! Don't malign yourself... But what are you doing here in Elsinore? We'll teach you a thing or two about drinking, before you leave!

Horatio I came to your father's funeral.

Hamlet Don't mock me, fellow student. You mean, you came to my mother's wedding!

Horatio Well, it did follow hot on its heels.

Hamlet Good housekeeping, Horatio! The hot food at the funeral became the cold buffet for the wedding. I wish I had died before seeing that day, Horatio. My father! I think I can see my father!

Horatio [*Looking around, startled*] Where, my lord?

Hamlet In my mind's eye, Horatio.

Horatio I saw him once. He was a fine king.

Hamlet He was a man. I won't see *his* like again.

Horatio My lord, I think I saw him last night.

Hamlet Saw? Who?

Horatio The King, your father.

Hamlet [*Incredulously*] My father?

Horatio Keep calm! Listen, I have something extraordinary to tell you. On two successive nights, while these gentlemen were on guard, a figure looking just like your father and in armour marched slowly past close by them—three times!—while they watched, in dumb horror. They told me this in strict secrecy, and last night I kept guard with them, and the ghost appeared again looking exactly as they had described it. I recognised your father, no question of it.

Hamlet But where was this?

Horatio On the castle wall where we were on guard, my lord.

Hamlet Didn't you speak to it?

Horatio Yes, but it didn't answer. At one point it looked as if it was about to speak, but then the cock crowed and it disappeared.

Hamlet How strange!

Horatio I swear it's true, my lord, and we felt it was our duty to tell you.

Hamlet Yes, of course. This is serious. [*To **Marcellus** and **Bernardo***] Are you on guard tonight?

Marcellus & **Bernardo** Yes, my lord.

Hamlet In armour, you say?

Marcellus Yes.

Hamlet From top to toe?

Bernardo From head to foot, my lord.

Hamlet So you didn't see his face?

Horatio Oh yes, my lord. His visor was up.

Hamlet And how did he look? Angry? Pale?

Horatio More sad than angry, my lord, and very pale.

Hamlet I wish I'd been there.

Horatio You'd have been shocked.

Hamlet Yes, very likely. His beard was grey, no?

Horatio Exactly as it used to be. Black, with streaks of grey.

Hamlet I'll join you tonight. Perhaps it will walk again.

Horatio I'm sure it will.

Hamlet If it looks at all like my father, I'll speak to it, and the devil himself won't stop me! Please continue to keep this to yourselves, and whatever happens tonight, note it carefully but say nothing. I'd appreciate that very much. Goodbye. I'll come between eleven and twelve.

Horatio You can depend on our loyalty.

Hamlet On your *friendship!* Goodbye. [***Horatio, Marcellus,** and **Bernardo** go out*] My father's ghost in armour! All is not well. I suspect foul play, but truth will out!

Scene 3

A room in Polonius' house

[*Laertes and Ophelia come in*]

Laertes My things are on board, so I'll say goodbye. And sister, when there's a ship going to France, write to me.

Ophelia Of course.

Laertes And about Hamlet and his flirting, just look on it as a passing fancy, a young man's infatuation, nothing more.

Ophelia Are you sure?

Laertes Nothing more. As a man grows older, his horizons widen. Perhaps Hamlet really does love you now, and his intentions are honourable, but consider his position as a Prince. He is not free to choose like an ordinary citizen; the welfare and safety of the state depend on him. So if he says he loves you, you would be wise to believe it only so far as his circumstances and the people of Denmark allow. And consider how your reputation will suffer if you lose your heart to him, or your body! Watch out, dear sister! You can't be too careful. Even saints are not safe from slander. Spring buds can be blighted even before they open, so fear the worst. Youth is a passionate time!

Ophelia I will take your advice to heart. But don't be like a bad priest, brother, and show *me* the steep and difficult way to heaven while *you* follow the primrose path.

Laertes Don't worry about me. [*He sees Polonius coming*] I'm late. Here comes father. [*Polonius comes in and Laertes kneels in front of him*] Now I can have a second blessing!

Polonius Still here, Laertes? You should be on board! The wind is right and they are waiting for you. There! My blessing. [*He lays his hands on Laertes' head*] Now, I want you to bear these few things in mind. Always keep your thoughts to yourself, and think carefully before you act. Be friendly but not too familiar, and when you make good friends be sure to cherish them—and don't waste a lot of time making new friends! Avoid getting involved in quarrels, but once in, be sure to keep the upper hand. Be a good listener, but say little yourself. Be prepared to accept criticism, but never be tempted to judge others. Dress as well as you can, but not showily; the clothes often reveal the man, as you will see from the way the best people dress in France. Neither lend money nor borrow it; loans can lose you both money and friends, and borrowing is a sign of bad

8

management. Above all, be true to yourself; you will then be false to no one. Goodbye, and God bless you.

Laertes Goodbye, my lord. Goodbye, Ophelia. And remember what I said.

Ophelia I will. I promise I will.

Laertes Goodbye. [*He goes out*]

Polonius What did he say to you, Ophelia?

Ophelia Something about Lord Hamlet.

Polonius That's good. I'm told that he has been meeting you lately in private, and that you have been only too happy to see him. If it's true, what people are saying, you must be more aware of your position as my daughter and a respectable girl. What is there between you? Tell me the truth.

Ophelia He's been telling me how much he likes me.

Polonius "Likes". Pooh! You're talking like a schoolgirl. Do you mean you believe him?

Ophelia I don't know what to think.

Polonius I'll tell you, then. It's childish to be taken in by foolish nothings. Don't fool around, or you'll make a fool of *me*.

Ophelia My lord, he has offered me his love honourably, and has sworn to me by heaven—

Polonius Yes, traps to catch silly mice! I know how freely the tongue makes promises when the blood is on fire. Such flames give more light than heat, daughter. There's no fire there. From now on, keep yourself to yourself, be more reserved. As for Lord Hamlet, he is a young man and can enjoy more freedom than you. In short, do not believe his promises of love, Ophelia, they're a fraud, a shameless show put on to deceive you, you mustn't trust them. Now listen! I forbid you to waste any more of your time with Lord Hamlet. Don't forget! Come along now.

Ophelia Yes, my lord.

Scene 4

The castle wall

| Hamlet |
| Horatio |
| Marcellus |
| (Ghost) |

[***Hamlet**, **Horatio**, and **Marcellus** come in*]

Hamlet It's bitterly cold.

Horatio Yes, there's a nip in the air.

Hamlet What's the time?

Horatio Just before midnight, I think.

9

Marcellus No, the clock has already struck.

Horatio Has it? I didn't hear it. It's about now that the spirit usually appears. [*Trumpets and drums are heard*] What's going on?

Hamlet The King's up late tonight, drinking and feasting and dancing. They make that din whenever he proposes a toast.

Horatio Is it a Danish custom?

Hamlet Yes, but even though I was brought up to it, I think it's a custom best forgotten. It gives us Danes a bad name abroad; they just call us drunkards and pigs, so that even our finest achievements aren't recognised. And it's the same with an individual: some innate defect, something a man can't help and can't really be blamed for, overshadows what's good in him. That one blemish can ruin his entire reputation, however pure, however virtuous he may be otherwise—

Horatio Look, my lord! Here it comes!

[*The **Ghost** comes in*]

Hamlet God help us! [*To the **Ghost***] Are you from heaven or hell? Good or evil? What should I call you? "Hamlet"? "King"? "Father"? "Royal Dane"...? Answer me! I *must* know... You were buried with due ceremony, so why has the grave thrown you up again? What does it mean? Why have you come back dressed in armour, to haunt and terrify us poor mortals out of our wits? Tell me why! Tell me what we should do! [*The **Ghost** beckons to **Hamlet***]

Horatio It wants you to go with it. It wants to speak to you on your own.

Marcellus How courteously it's beckoning to you! But you mustn't go...

Horatio No, you mustn't.

Hamlet It won't speak to me here, so I'll follow it.

Horatio Don't go, my lord.

Hamlet What's there to be afraid of? I don't care a damn about my life, and what can it do to my immortal soul? I'll follow it.

Horatio What if it tempts you towards the sea or the overhanging cliffs, my lord, and takes on some other horrible shape and drives you mad? Just being on that cliff is enough to make a man desperate, with the sea way down below and the roar of the waves.

Hamlet It's still beckoning to me. [*To the **Ghost***] Go on! I'll follow you.

Marcellus You won't, my lord. [*He holds **Hamlet***]

Hamlet Take your hands off me!

Horatio Listen! You mustn't go! [*He helps to hold **Hamlet***]

Hamlet My fate calls out to me and gives me courage! [*The **Ghost** beckons to him*] It's calling me again. [*To **Horatio** and **Marcellus***] Let go, gentlemen! By heaven, I'll make *you* into ghosts if you stop me! Get out of my way! [*He pushes them away and speaks to the **Ghost***] Go on! I'll follow you! [***Hamlet** follows the **Ghost** out*]

Horatio What a desperate state he's in!

Marcellus Let's follow him. We shouldn't have listened to him. Something is rotten in the state of Denmark!

Scene 5

Another part of the wall

Hamlet
Ghost
Horatio
Marcellus

[*The **Ghost** and **Hamlet** come in*]

Hamlet Where are you taking me? Speak to me!

Ghost Listen! My time is almost up. I must return to hell.

Hamlet Poor ghost!

Ghost I don't need your pity. Just listen!

Hamlet I am ready.

Ghost Ready to take revenge?

Hamlet Revenge?

Ghost I am your father's ghost, doomed to walk by night and suffer by day until all my sins are cleansed. I could tell you a story to tear your soul apart, freeze your young blood and make your eyes start out of your head, but such secrets are not for human ears. Listen! If you loved your father—

Hamlet Oh, God!

Ghost —revenge his foul murder!

Hamlet Murder?

Ghost A foul, strange and unnatural murder.

Hamlet Tell me, so my revenge can be as swift as thought!

Ghost Good. You'd have to be drugged out of your senses not to be stirred by this. Now listen, Hamlet! The people of Denmark have been told that while I was sleeping in my orchard, a snake bit me. They have been grossly misled. The snake that took your father's life now wears his crown!

Hamlet I suspected it—my uncle!

11

Ghost Yes, that incestuous, adulterous beast, whose tricks and bribes seduced my apparently virtuous Queen! Oh, Hamlet, what a fall that was! To go from a loving and faithful husband to a wretch like him. But then virtue and vice will always be true to themselves... [*Looking up*] I can smell the morning air, I must be brief. While I was sleeping in my orchard—I thought I was safe there—your uncle poured poison in my ear. It worked quickly, and at one stroke my brother took my life, my crown and my Queen; killed me before I had a chance to confess my sins and make my peace with God. Horrible! If you have any feelings, do not allow the good name of Denmark to be dishonoured. But as for your mother, leave her to her own conscience. Goodbye! Morning is near. Goodbye! Remember me! [*The **Ghost** disappears*]

Hamlet Oh, heavens above! Oh, my heart! But I must be strong! Remember you! Yes, poor ghost, I will, as long as memory lasts in here. [*He holds his head*] I'll wipe the slate clean of all the things I've read, or seen, or thought. Your wishes alone shall occupy my mind. I swear it! You wicked woman, you damned, smiling hypocrite! Let me make a note of that: in Denmark, you can smile and smile and be a villain... So there you are, uncle! Now, what did he say? "Goodbye, goodbye. Remember me!" Oh yes, I will!

[***Horatio** and **Marcellus** come in. They do not see **Hamlet** at first*]

Horatio [*Calling*] My lord, my lord—

Marcellus Lord Hamlet!

Horatio I hope he's safe. [*Calling*] Are you there, my lord?

Hamlet [*Imitating him*] Are you there, my lord?

Marcellus How are you, my lord?

Horatio What news?

Hamlet Wonderful news!

Horatio [*After a pause*] Tell us, then.

Hamlet No! You'll tell the others.

Horatio [*Indignantly*] Certainly not, my lord.

Hamlet Well, there isn't a villain in Denmark... who isn't rotten!

Horatio You don't need a ghost to come from the grave to tell you that!

Hamlet Quite right. Yes, you're right. So we'll say goodbye. You must go and do what you have to—we've all got something we need to do, I suppose—and I, I'll go and pray.

Horatio But this is nonsense...

Hamlet I'm sorry! I've offended you, I'm sorry.

Horatio No one's offended, my lord.

Hamlet Oh, yes they are, Horatio, they certainly are... Now, about this ghost. It is an honest ghost, I can tell you that. As to what's happened, you'll just have to contain your curiosity... [*Pause*] Friends, do one thing for me: don't tell anyone what you have seen tonight.

Horatio & **Marcellus** Of course we won't, my lord.

Hamlet Swear that you won't. On my sword!

Ghost [*From under the stage*] Swear!

Hamlet [*To the **Ghost***] Ah, you agree, do you? [*To **Horatio** and **Marcellus***] Come on! You've heard the fellow in the cellar! You must swear.

Horatio Swear to what, my lord?

Hamlet Never to say what you've seen.

Ghost [*From below another part of the stage*] Swear!

Hamlet That's right, old mole! How fast you dig! [*He moves to another part of the stage*] Come here, friends.

Horatio Stranger and stranger!

Hamlet Then welcome it as you would a stranger! Your science can't explain everything, Horatio... Now promise, however strangely I behave, whatever act I put on, promise me that you'll never let on—either by a hint or a gesture or some significant phrase such as "We know..." or "We could tell you..."—that you know what I'm up to. Swear that you never will!

Ghost [*Underneath*] Swear!

Hamlet Rest, poor spirit, rest! [***Horatio** and **Marcellus** each place a hand on **Hamlet**'s sword and swear that they "will never tell anyone what they have seen tonight"*] Thank you, gentlemen, thank you. Whatever poor Hamlet can do to show his love and friendship will be done. Let's go in together. [*He puts a finger to his lips*] Don't forget! [*To himself*] The world's gone mad! Why do *I* have to be the one to put things right? [*To the others*] Come, we'll go in.

ACT TWO

Scene 1

A room in Polonius' house, some days later

[**Polonius** *and his servant* **Reynaldo** *come in*]

Polonius Give him this money and these letters, Reynaldo.

Reynaldo Yes, my lord.

Polonius And before you visit him, I'd like you to make some enquiries about him.

Reynaldo I was going to, my lord.

Polonius Excellent, excellent. Now, first of all, I want you to find out what Danish people there are in Paris: who they are, where they live, what they do, who their friends are, what they spend their money on. And when, in this roundabout way, you've gathered that they know my son, let on that you too have some slight acquaintance with him. Say you know his father and some of his friends, for example. Do you follow me, Reynaldo?

Reynaldo Perfectly well, my lord.

Polonius Say something like, "I only know him a little, but the person I'm thinking of is pretty wild and addicted to—" Make up what you like about him, but nothing too offensive, mind; the sort of mischief that young men get up to when they are away from home.

Reynaldo Like gambling, my lord?

Polonius Yes, or drinking, fencing, quarrelling, women. You can go as far as that.

Reynaldo But that *would* be offensive, my lord.

Polonius Yes, you'd better play that down. I don't mean you should say he's immoral. But describe his faults cunningly, so that they seem to be the—er—natural expressions of a fiery nature.

Reynaldo [*Puzzled*] But, my lord—

Polonius You're wondering why you should do all this?

Reynaldo Yes, my lord. I would like to know.

Polonius My idea is this, and I think it's a legitimate ruse. You accuse my son of these slight indiscretions, and the person you are addressing, having seen the young man referred to committing the aforementioned crimes, will end by confiding in you and speak as follows, "My dear sir—" or "My friend—" or just "Sir—", according to the custom of the country... [*He hesitates*]

14

Reynaldo Yes, my lord?

Polonius And then he... he then... Dammit! I was about to say something. Where had I got to?

Reynaldo To "Confiding in you" and "My dear sir".

Polonius Ah yes, "Confiding in you". He'll finish like this: "I know the young man, I saw him yesterday", or whenever, "with so-and-so; gambling, drunk or quarrelling at a night-club". Or perhaps, "I saw him going into a brothel..." So, you see, your lie will fish out the truth. That's how we clever people get there, the circuitous, roundabout way. You understand?

Reynaldo Yes, my lord.

Polonius Goodbye then, and good luck.

Reynaldo My lord. [*He bows*]

Polonius Observe him yourself, as well.

Reynaldo I shall, my lord. [*He goes out*]

[*Ophelia comes running in looking very upset*]

Polonius What's the matter, Ophelia?

Ophelia Oh, my lord, I've had such a fright. I was in my room sewing, when Lord Hamlet—with his clothes all dirty and dishevelled, and looking pale and haunted as if he'd been to hell and back—came right up to me...

Polonius Mad for your love?

Ophelia I don't know, my lord, but I'm afraid so.

Polonius What did he say?

Ophelia Nothing, my lord. He just grabbed my wrist and then stood back, holding me at arm's length, studying my face for a long time as if he were going to draw me. At last he moved his head up and down, like this, and let out a terrible sigh; it seemed to tear him apart. Then he let go of my arm and went out, still looking at me over his shoulder.

Polonius Come along, we must go and find the King. This is the madness of love! Passion can drive a man to desperate things. I am sorry... [*Accusingly*] Have you spoken roughly to him lately?

Ophelia No, my lord. But I did what you told me, and refused to see him or even accept his letters.

Polonius That's driven him mad! I wish I'd understood him better. I thought he was just playing around, and meant to ruin you. Damn my suspicious mind! But then we older people are inclined to be over-cautious, just as the young tend to be too impulsive. We must go and tell the King, and risk the consequences.

15

King	Voltemand
Queen	(Cornelius)
Rosencrantz	Hamlet
Guildenstern	1st Actor
(Attendants)	(Other Actors)
Polonius	

Scene 2
A room in the castle

[*The **King** and **Queen** come in with **Rosencrantz, Guildenstern** and some Attendants*]

King Welcome, Rosencrantz and Guildenstern! We have of course been wanting to see you, but we have sent for you urgently because we need your help. You will have heard about Hamlet's "transformation"; I call it that since he's neither outwardly nor inwardly the man he was. But what—other than his father's death—has upset him so much, I have no idea. Since you grew up with him and know him well, be so kind as to stay here at court for a while. Encourage him to enjoy himself, and find out if there's anything troubling him that we're unaware of, and that we might be able to help him with.

Queen He's talked about you a great deal, and I'm sure there's no one else he's as close to. If you will be so kind as to spend some time with us and help us, you will be royally rewarded.

Rosencrantz Your majesties might well have ordered us, not asked us.

Guildenstern But we obey. We put ourselves at your service.

King Thank you, Rosencrantz and Guildenstern.

Queen Thank you. Please visit our poor son straight away. [*To the Attendants*] Take these gentlemen to Hamlet!

Guildenstern I hope he will find it pleasant and helpful to have us with him.

Queen Yes, I hope so.

[***Rosencrantz** and **Guildenstern** go out with some of the **Attendants**. **Polonius** comes in and speaks to the **King***]

Polonius The ambassadors are back from Norway, my lord. They've been successful.

King Ah, you always bring good news!

Polonius Do I, my lord? Well, I do my best to be loyal to my God and my King. And I think—unless this politician's brain of mine is not as astute as it used to be—that I have discovered the cause of Hamlet's madness.

King Go on, then. Tell me!

16

Polonius Admit the ambassadors first. My news can round off the feast.

King Begin it yourself then, and bring them in. [***Polonius** goes out*] My dear, he says he has discovered the cause of your son's madness.

Queen I suspect it's for the obvious reasons: his father's death, and our hasty marriage.

King Well, we'll soon find out. [***Polonius** comes in again with **Voltemand** and **Cornelius***] Welcome, friends! Well, Voltemand, what does the King of Norway have to say?

Voltemand He returns your greetings, your Majesty, and has done what you requested: he has stopped his nephew's preparations, which appeared to be against the Poles but were in fact against your Highness. The King was so hurt by his nephew's deception that he issued orders against him. When Fortinbras accepted his uncle's rebuke and promised never to threaten your Majesty again, the Norwegian King was so delighted that he gave his nephew three thousand crowns a year, and told him to go and attack Poland. [*He gives the **King** a paper*] Here is a request for free passage for his army through your country.

King Excellent! I'll study it at leisure. Meanwhile, thank you for a job well done. Go and rest now, and tonight we will have a feast. Welcome home! [***Voltemand** and **Cornelius** go out*]

Polonius A satisfactory ending. [*He takes a deep breath*] My Lord and Madam, to discuss what kingship ought to be, what duty is, why day is day, night is night and time is time, would be merely to waste night, day and time. Therefore, since brevity is the soul of wit, I will be brief. Your noble son is mad. And to be mad is—simply—to be mad. But never mind that.

Queen More fact and less fancy, if you please.

Polonius Madam, there's nothing fanciful about me! That he's mad is true. And truly that's a pity. And it's a pity that it's true: a foolish play on words, I must stop it. So he's mad, and now we need to find the cause of this effect, or rather, defect. Hm! I have a daughter—as long as she is mine—who quite rightly gave me this. [*He reads from a letter*] "To the heavenly and most beautified Ophelia..." Ugh! "Beautified". That's dreadful! [*He reads*] "In her excellent white bosom these etcetera."

Queen Did Hamlet send her this?

Polonius Wait, madam, please. I'll read what's here. [*He reads*]
> "Doubt that the stars are fire,
> Doubt there's a God above,
> Call holy truth a liar,
> But never doubt my love!

Oh Ophelia, I can't put my passion into poetry, but you must believe me when I say that I love you deeply, with all my heart. Goodbye! Yours for evermore, while the wheels turn, Hamlet."
My daughter, obedient girl that she is, gave me this, and she has told me about every one of his approaches to her

King But how did she respond to him?

Polonius What do you take me for?

King A loyal and honourable man.

Polonius [*He bows*] I sincerely hope so. But what would you think, sir, if I had seen this passion burning—as I did, even before my daughter told me—what would you, or the Queen here, think if I had played the pandar, or turned a blind eye? No! I went straight to work and said to my daughter: "Lord Hamlet is a Prince, and not for you", and ordered her not to see him or accept anything from him. She took my advice, and he—repulsed—became depressed, stopped eating, stopped sleeping, grew weak, and then light-headed, and finally fell into the raving madness that we are so unhappy about.

King [*To the Queen*] Do you think he is right?

Queen Quite likely.

Polonius Have I ever been wrong in the past?

King Not that I know of.

Polonius [*Pointing to his head and shoulders*] Take this from this if I'm wrong! If there's evidence, I'll ferret out the truth!

King But what more can we do?

Polonius You know he sometimes walks up and down here for hours? [*The Queen nods*] That's when I'll set my daughter on him. We'll hide over there [*he points*] and watch them. If he hasn't gone mad for love of her, I'll give up politics and take up farming!

King We'll try it.

Queen [*Looking off stage*] Here comes the poor creature, deep in a book.

Polonius [*To the King and Queen*] Please go and hide. I'll approach him. Leave it to me. [*The **King**, **Queen** and **Attendants** hurry out. **Hamlet** comes in, reading a book*] How are you, Lord Hamlet?

Hamlet Well, thank you.

Polonius Do you know who I am, my lord?

Hamlet Yes, of course. You're a salesman!

Polonius Certainly not, my lord!

Hamlet Then I wish you were as honest as one.

18

Polonius Honest, my lord?

Hamlet Yes, an honest man is one in a million in this wicked world.

Polonius That's true, my lord.

Hamlet If the sun can breed maggots in a dead dog... Have you got a daughter?

Polonius Yes, my lord.

Hamlet Don't let her walk in the sun. Conception is a blessing, but watch out for your daughter! [*He goes on reading*]

Polonius [*To himself*] What's this? Still on about my daughter? But he didn't recognise me at first, thought I was a salesman. He's far gone, and yet I remember how I myself used to suffer for love when I was young, almost as much as this. I'll speak to him again. [*To **Hamlet***] What are you reading, my lord?

Hamlet Words, words, words!

Polonius What is the matter?

Hamlet With whom?

Polonius I mean, what's the *subject* matter!

Hamlet Slander, sir. The impertinent fellow says here that old men have grey beards, that they have gummy eyes and wrinkly faces, and that they are weak in the head and the legs; and though I'm sure he's right, I don't think it ought to be put into print. Do you know, you'd be my age if you could—like a crab—go backwards! [*He goes on reading*]

Polonius [*To himself*] How pointed some of his replies are, but then madness is like that. I'll go and arrange for him to meet my daughter. [*To **Hamlet***] My honourable lord, I take my leave.

Hamlet There's nothing I'd be happier for you to take, except my life, my life…

Polonius Goodbye, sir.

Hamlet [*To himself*] These tedious old fools!

[*As **Polonius** goes out he speaks to **Rosencrantz** and **Guildenstern**, who are coming in*]

Polonius You're looking for Lord Hamlet? There he is!

Rosencrantz Thank you, sir.

Rosencrantz & **Guildenstern** [*To **Hamlet**, bowing*] My lord!

Hamlet [*Shaking hands with them*] How are you, Guildenstern? Ah, Rosencrantz! How are you, my friends?

Rosencrantz We're all right. Nothing special.

Guildenstern Not exactly up in the clouds.

Hamlet A bit low in your fortunes?

Rosencrantz Not really low, my lord.

Hamlet Nearer Fortune's middle, eh? They say Lady Luck's quite a girl... [*He speaks seriously*] Now, what's your news?

Rosencrantz Just that the world's grown honest.

Hamlet Then the end is near! But you're lying... I'll be more specific. Why has Fortune sent you to prison?

Guildenstern Prison, my lord?

Hamlet Denmark's a prison.

Rosencrantz Then the world is one.

Hamlet A large one, with many cells, and Denmark is one of the worst.

Rosencrantz We don't think so, my lord.

Hamlet Well then, for you it isn't, since it's our thoughts that make things good or bad. For me, it's a prison.

Rosencrantz That's because you're ambitious. It's too narrow for your *mind*.

Hamlet Good God! I could live inside a nutshell and think it was the universe, except for my bad dreams.

Guildenstern Such dreams suggest ambition, which is itself only the shadow of a dream.

Hamlet But dreams themselves are mere shadows.

Rosencrantz Then ambition is simply the shadow of a shadow.

Hamlet In that case only beggars are real, and kings and heroes are *their* shadows... Shall we go in? My head's spinning.

Rosencrantz & Guildenstern [*Bowing*] We are your servants.

Hamlet No, don't call yourselves servants, mine are terrible! Tell me, between old friends, what are you doing in Elsinore?

Rosencrantz Visiting you, my lord. That's all.

Hamlet I suppose I ought to thank you, though my thanks aren't worth much. [*Sharply*] Were you sent for? Was it your own idea? Come on, be honest with me. [*They say nothing*] Well?

Guildenstern What is there to say, my lord?

Hamlet [*Sarcastically*] Anything, so long as it's pointless... You *were* sent for! I can see it in your faces, you're not clever enough to hide it. I know that the good King and Queen sent for you.

Rosencrantz What for, my lord?

Hamlet That's for *you* to tell *me*! I appeal to you, in the name of our long and devoted friendship etcetera, be open with me. Were you sent for or not? [*He walks away*]

Rosencrantz [*To **Guildenstern***] What shall we say? [*They talk*]

Hamlet [*To himself*] I'm watching you! [*To **Rosencrantz** and **Guildenstern***] Please answer!

Guildenstern My lord, we were sent for.

Hamlet And I'll tell you why, to save you having to break your promise to the King and Queen. [*He sighs*] I have been feeling so low lately, I don't know why. The world seems a deadly place to me, the sky just a pall of pollution. What an astonishing creature a man is, so godlike in his thoughts, so wide-ranging in his accomplishments! He is the lord of creation, gracing the world with his beauty! And yet what is this beautifully made bag of bones to me? Man sickens me—and woman too, whatever your smiles may say!

Rosencrantz I was thinking no such thing, my lord.

Hamlet [*Sharply*] Then why did you laugh when I said "Man sickens me"?

Rosencrantz I was thinking about the actors we met on our way here, that they won't get much of a welcome.

Hamlet I'll make sure that the one that plays the king does: his majesty shall be well rewarded! And the knight will put his sword to good use, the lover won't sigh in vain, the clown will get his laughs, and the lady will speak her mind and spoil the verse! What actors are they?

Rosencrantz Your favourites, the Wittenburg Players.

Hamlet Are they still popular? Or have they grown rusty?

Rosencrantz No, they're as good as ever. [*Trumpets are heard*] Aha! They've arrived.

Hamlet [*To **Rosencrantz** and **Guildenstern***] Welcome to Elsinore! Come, let me shake you by the hand and welcome you properly. There! I mustn't treat you worse than the actors... But my "uncle-father" and "aunt-mother" are mistaken.

Guildenstern About what, my lord?

Hamlet I'm only mad when the wind's in the north. I can tell what's what!

[***Polonius** comes in*]

Polonius Hello, gentlemen! [*He busies himself with something, while **Hamlet** and the others talk about him*]

Hamlet Listen, Guildenstern, and [*to **Rosencrantz***] you too; that great baby isn't out of his nappies yet.

Rosencrantz Perhaps he's in his second childhood!

Hamlet You'll see! He's coming to tell me about the actors. [*To **Polonius***] You're right, sir! On Monday morning.

Polonius My lord, I've got news for you.

Hamlet [*Imitating him*] My lord, I've got news for you!

Polonius The actors are here, my lord.

Hamlet [*He sings*] "Then came each actor on his ass..."

Polonius The best actors in the world for tragedy, comedy, history, tragicomedy, tragi-history, historical comedy, tragi-comic-history, or poetry unlimited.

Hamlet What a treasure Mrs Porter had!

Polonius What treasure was that?

Hamlet [*He sings*] Mrs Porter and her daughter
                Wash their feet in soda water!

Polonius [*To himself*] Still on about my daughter.

Hamlet Isn't that right, Mr Porter?

Polonius I may not be Mr Porter, my lord, but I have a daughter that I love very much.

Hamlet No, that doesn't follow... But look over there, and you'll see what does. [*The **Actors** come in*] Welcome! I'm glad to see you all. [*To the **First Actor**, who has a beard*] My old friend! You've gone under cover since I last saw you! [*To the **Second Actor**, a young man who plays women's parts*] Young lady! You've grown up since I last saw you, but I hope your voice hasn't gone down. You are all welcome! Let's jump straight in. Show us what you can do. What about a speech? One with a bit of passion in it!

First Actor What speech, my lord?

Hamlet I remember one from a rather fine play that wasn't very popular. It's where Aeneas tells his story to Dido, especially the bit where he describes the death of Priam. If you can remember it, start at [*he hesitates*] let me see, let me see...
         "Now sturdy Pyrrhus, like a Bengal Tiger..."
No, that's not right, but it does begin with Pyrrhus...
         "Now sturdy Pyrrhus, armed in sombre black—
           Dark was his evil mind, dark as the night
           When he lay waiting in the wooden horse—
           With gruesome blood is smeared from head to foot,
           The blood of fathers, mothers, daughters, sons,
           Murdered so cruelly in the streets of Troy.

> Coated with gore, his eyes on fire, Pyrrhus
> Hunts for old Priam..."

[*To the* **First Actor**] You go on.

Polonius That was good, my lord, very well spoken.

First Actor "Soon Pyrrhus finds him,
> Too weak to raise his sword. So Pyrrhus strikes
> But in his rage the blow goes wide. Even so
> The swing of it brings Priam crashing down.
> But look! Held by the sight, Pyrrhus stands
> With sword in air, a tyrant in a picture
> Doing nothing.
> Then calm gives way to storm, as Pyrrhus brings
> His bleeding sword, unfeeling as a hammer
> That forges iron to make the strongest armour,
> Down upon Priam.
> Oh treacherous Fortune! May the gods
> Take all your power away and break your wheel
> And hurl it down to hell!"

Polonius That was too long.

Hamlet We'll send it to the barber's with your beard! [*To the* **First Actor**] Go on, please. He only likes comedies or dirty stories, otherwise he goes to sleep. Get on to Hecuba.

First Actor "But who, oh who that saw the muffled Queen—"

Hamlet The "muffled Queen"?

Polonius That's good! "Muffled Queen" is good!

First Actor "—run barefoot up and down, damping the flames
> With floods of tears, no crown upon her head
> But a mere scarf, a blanket for a shawl:
> Whoever witnessed this would surely rail
> Against blind Fate; even the gods themselves—
> Knowing that Hecuba had seen cruel Pyrrhus
> Make mincemeat of her husband with his sword—
> Would pity feel, hearing her dreadful cries,
> And the stars would weep."

Polonius Look! He's gone pale, he's got tears in his eyes! Please stop!

Hamlet [*To the* **First Actor**] All right, you can recite the rest later. [*To **Polonius**] My lord, please look after the actors, look after them well. They mirror our times. Better a bad obituary than a scandal during one's lifetime.

23

Polonius My lord, I'll treat them as they deserve.

Hamlet Good heavens, man! Better, much better! If we got what we deserved, which of us would escape punishment? Treat them as *you'd* expect to be treated, then the less they deserve the greater your kindness. Take them in.

Polonius [*To the Actors*] Come, gentlemen!

Hamlet Follow him, friends. [*As the Actors go out with Polonius, Hamlet stops the First Actor*] Listen, old friend. Can you put on "The Murder of Gonzago"?

First Actor Yes, my lord.

Hamlet We'll have it tonight. You could learn a speech of ten or twelve lines if I insert it into the play, couldn't you?

First Actor Yes, my lord.

Hamlet Very well. Follow that Lord, but don't make fun of him! [*The First Actor goes out and Hamlet speaks to Rosencrantz and Guildenstern*] Friends, I'll see you tonight. You are welcome to Elsinore.

Rosencrantz Thank you, my lord. [*They go out*]

Hamlet [*To himself*] What a cheat and a coward I am! To think that a mere *actor* can work himself into such a pretence of passion that his voice falters, his face turns pale and tears come into his eyes! And all for nothing! For Hecuba! What's Hecuba to him or he to Hecuba that he should weep for her? Imagine what he would do if he had *my* cause for passion! He would flood the stage with tears, fill the air with his rantings, confront the guilty, shock the innocent, confuse the ignorant! But I—dull, useless dreamer that I am—just mope and say nothing, not even for a murdered king. Am I a coward? Do they insult me, assault me, call me a downright liar? Do they? Then I should bloody well accept it. If I wasn't the most despicable coward alive, I would have thrown his guts to the crows, the filthy, dirty villain! Treacherous, lecherous, inhuman beast! Revenge! [*Pause*] What an ass I am! Isn't it marvellous that the son of a murdered father, with every reason for revenge, should show his feelings in a mere torrent of futile curses? Ugh! Let me think... I have heard that guilty people have been so moved by a cleverly written play that they have confessed their crimes. Murder will out! I'll get these actors to do a scene something like the murder of my father. I'll observe my uncle closely, and if he flinches I'll know what to do. The ghost I've seen could well be the devil, out to deceive me and damn me and take advantage of my weakness and misery. I'll use the play to catch the king!

ACT THREE

Scene 1
A room in the castle

King
Queen
Rosencrantz
Guildenstern
Polonius
Ophelia
(Lords)
Hamlet

[*The **King** and **Queen**, **Rosencrantz**, **Guildenstern**, **Polonius**, **Ophelia** and some **Lords** come in*]

King Surely you could ask a few discreet questions and find out why he's behaving so strangely?

Rosencrantz He admits he's upset, but won't say why.

Guildenstern We don't find him very forthcoming, Sir. A sort of cunning madness prevents us from getting at his real feelings.

Queen Was he friendly?

Rosencrantz He was very polite.

Guildenstern But it did seem quite an effort for him.

Rosencrantz He didn't say very much, but was willing to answer our questions.

Queen Did you manage to get him interested in any amusements?

Rosencrantz Yes, Madam. We happened to overtake some actors on our way here, so we told him about them. He appeared to be quite interested—in fact, they are somewhere in the castle now, and he has asked them to perform for him tonight.

Polonius That's right. And he has asked me to invite you to the performance.

King It will be a pleasure. I'm delighted to hear it. You must go on encouraging him.

Rosencrantz We shall, my lord.

[***Rosencrantz, Guildenstern** and the **Lords** go out*]

King My dear Gertrude, will you leave us too, please? We've arranged for Hamlet to meet Ophelia here, as if by accident. Polonius and I—quite legitimately, I think—intend to spy on them so that we can tell whether it is love that is at the root of his unhappiness.

Queen I'll go. Oh, Ophelia, I do hope it is your beauty that is the cause of his wild behaviour, and I pray that your good sense will bring him back to his old self again, for both your sakes.

Ophelia I hope so too, Madam.

[*The **Queen** goes out*]

25

Polonius Ophelia, you walk along here. [*To the **King***] And we'll position ourselves over here, your Majesty. [*To **Ophelia***] Look at this prayer book; that will explain your being here on your own. A show of piety can make even the devil look pleasant!

King How true! [*To himself*] How guilty he makes me feel! Here I am, covering up my ugly deed with fine words, like a prostitute painting her face! [*He sighs*] Ah me!

[*The **King** and **Polonius** hide. **Hamlet** comes in*]

Hamlet [*To himself*] What should I do? Endure this anguish and torment, or simply end it all? If death is nothing more than sleep—an end to heartache and suffering—that's a prize worth praying for! [*He sighs*] To die, to sleep! But what if we should dream? Ah, there's the rub! Who knows what dreams may come in that sleep of death? It is this that makes us drag out our wretched lives. Why else would ordinary, decent people put up with pain and sorrow, with rudeness, oppression and injustice, when they could so easily end it all? Who in his right mind would groan and sweat his way through this weary world, unless the fear of something after death made him hesitate and decide to put up with the troubles he already knows? So it's our thoughts that turn us into cringing cowards, and even the greatest enterprises come to nothing. [*He sees **Ophelia** praying, and speaks to himself*] Gently now! [*To **Ophelia***] Remember me in your prayers, sweet lady!

Ophelia My lord, how have you been keeping?

Hamlet Well, thank you. Well!

Ophelia These presents you gave me, my lord, I have been wanting to return them to you for some time. [*Offering them to him*] Please take them.

Hamlet I never gave you anything.

Ophelia You know you did, my lord, and you spoke to me in a way that made them especially precious. But even precious gifts become worthless when the giver proves unkind. Here they are!

Hamlet Aha!* Are you honest?

Ophelia My lord?

Hamlet Are you beautiful?

Ophelia What do you mean, sir?

Hamlet That if you were honest you wouldn't let men have anything to do with your beauty!

Ophelia Can beauty have a better companion than truth?

* Hamlet may have heard a noise from behind the curtains.

26

Hamlet Yes, it can, since beauty can seduce truth more easily than truth can reform beauty. Time has proved it...! I was in love with you once.

Ophelia You certainly made me think so, my lord.

Hamlet You shouldn't have believed me. Bad old habits die hard. I never loved you.

Ophelia So I was even more deceived.

Hamlet Get yourself to a nunnery! Why do you want to be a breeder of sinners? Look at me! I'm fairly honest, yet I'm guilty of such things that it would have been better if my mother had never borne me. I'm full of pride, I'm vindictive, ambitious... What are fellows like me doing here on this earth? We're all liars, don't believe any of us. Go to a nunnery. [*Suspiciously*] Where's your father?

Ophelia [*Hesitating*] He's... at home, my lord.

Hamlet Shut him up there, so that he can only play the fool in his own house. Goodbye! [*He starts going*]

Ophelia [*To herself*] Heaven help him!

Hamlet [*Turning back*] But if you do marry, I give you this warning: however pure or virtuous you are, you will never escape slander. Get yourself to a nunnery! Or if you must marry, marry a fool, since wise men know only too well what monsters you make of them! To a nunnery, quick! Goodbye!

Ophelia [*To herself*] Dear God, make him well again!

Hamlet And I know how you women paint yourselves. God has given you one face and you make another. You totter about on high heels, and lisp, and use silly names, and talk nonsense and make a virtue of it. I won't have it, it has made me mad! We will have no more marriages. Those who are married already, all except one, shall live; the rest shall stay as they are. To a nunnery, go! [*He goes out*]

Ophelia So it has come to this! A noble mind, utterly destroyed! He was such a gentleman, such a scholar and soldier, the hope of the nation, the idol of his age. His vows of love were like sweet music to me once, but there's nothing left now. Oh, to have seen all this, to see it now...!

[*The **King** and **Polonius** come in*]

King Love, indeed! He's not in love, and what he said, although it was a bit disjointed, didn't sound like madness. There's a brooding sadness in his soul which I fear may spell danger. To avoid trouble, this is what I've decided. He must go to England, to collect the taxes that are overdue. Travel and a change of scene may get rid of this obsession of his. What do you think?

Polonius It sounds a good idea, though I am still convinced that the real source of his grief is unrequited love. [*To **Ophelia***] Well, Ophelia! You don't have to tell us what Lord Hamlet said. We heard it all. [*To the **King***] My lord, do as you please. But if you think it's appropriate, let his mother see him privately after the play and try to get him to confide in her. Tell her to be firm with him, and I'll hide and listen. If she can't find out what the matter is, then send him to England or lock him up.

King Yes. We can't be too careful!

Scene 2

A large room in the castle

Hamlet	Horatio
1st Actor	King
Other Actors:	Queen
Prologue, King,	Ophelia
Queen, Lucianus	(Lords)
Polonius	(Attendants)
Rosencrantz	(Musicians)
Guildenstern	

[***Hamlet*** *comes in with the **Actors***]

Hamlet Say the speech exactly as I said it, please. Let it trip off your tongue lightly, don't mouth it! And another thing, don't saw the air with your hand like this. [*He demonstrates*] Even in the passionate parts, keep control. I hate seeing some rowdy fellow in a wig ranting and raving just to please the mob. Please avoid that sort of thing.

First Actor We will, my lord.

Hamlet But don't be too tame, either. Use your judgement. Make sure your actions suit your words, and your words your actions. Above all, be natural, since the point of a play is to mirror ourselves and our times, to reflect our virtues and our vices. Overacting, or a sloppy entrance, may get a cheap laugh, but it won't amuse discriminating theatregoers, and it is their criticism that counts. I've seen actors, very popular ones too, who moved and spoke so abominably that it looked as if they'd been put together by a bad workman!

First Actor I think we have made some improvements in that direction, sir.

Hamlet Go the whole way, please! And make sure your clowns don't put in jokes of their own and start some stupid people in the audience laughing just when an important point in the play needs stressing. That's unpardonable. It shows a sort of pathetic ambition in a clown... Go and get ready.

[*The **Actors** go out. **Polonius**, **Rosencrantz**, **Guildenstern** and **Horatio** come in*]

Hamlet [*To Polonius*] Hello! Will the King be watching this play?

Polonius Yes, and the Queen. They're on their way.

Hamlet Tell the actors to hurry. [*Polonius goes out. To Rosencrantz and Guildenstern*] You go too.

Rosencrantz & **Guildenstern** Yes, my lord. [*They go out*]

Hamlet Horatio, I know I can trust you as much as anyone I know.

Horatio My lord...

Hamlet No, don't think I'm flattering you. Anyway what do I stand to gain? You're not rich or famous, just a thoroughly good fellow, and what's the point of sucking up to the poor? Listen! Ever since I was old enough to judge, I've singled you out as my friend. I've seen the calm way you accept whatever life brings, good or bad, and a man who is master of his feelings is a man after my own heart. But enough of this. There's to be a play tonight, and the King will be there. One scene in it concerns what I told you about my father's death. While it is being acted, please watch my uncle closely. His guilt should show itself during one particular speech. If it doesn't, the ghost is a lying devil and my mind nothing but a cesspit. Observe him carefully, and I'll watch him too, and when the play is over we'll get together and discuss his reaction.

Horatio Yes, my lord. I won't let him get away with anything.

Hamlet Ah, here they are. I must get back to playing the madman. Find yourself a seat.

[*A march is played, and then a fanfare of trumpets. The **King** and **Queen** come in, followed by **Polonius**, **Ophelia**, **Rosencrantz**, **Guildenstern**, **Lords** and **Attendants**]

King How is our nephew Hamlet?

Hamlet Fat and happy! Full of empty promises!

King That's no answer!

Hamlet Nor is this! [*To Polonius*] Didn't you say you did some acting when you were at university?

Polonius Yes, I did, my lord, and I was considered rather good.

Hamlet What part did you play?

Polonius Julius Caesar. I was killed by Brutus and the others.

Hamlet What brutes they must have been! Are the actors ready?

Rosencrantz Yes, my lord, they are ready and waiting.

Queen Come here, Hamlet dear, and sit next to me.

Hamlet No, mother. [*Indicating Ophelia*] I'm more attracted to this.

29

Polonius Aha! [*Whispering to the King*] Did you hear that?

Hamlet [*To **Ophelia***] May I lie on your lap, lady?

Ophelia Certainly not, my lord.

Hamlet I mean, my head on your lap.

Ophelia Yes, my lord,

Hamlet Did you think I meant something rude?

Ophelia I thought nothing.

Hamlet Nothing between a girl's legs?

Ophelia You're always joking, my lord.

Hamlet What else is there to do? My mother looks cheerful enough, though my father died two hours ago.

Ophelia Two *months* ago, my lord.

Hamlet Good heavens! Died two months ago and still not forgotten? Then there's hope for great men, their memories may survive them by six months! But they'd better endow some foundation or other, or they'll have to put up with oblivion.

[*Music plays and the **Actors** mime the play that they are going to perform.* The Actor King and Actor Queen come in and embrace each other very lovingly. The Queen kneels down and appears to be declaring her love for the King. He raises her to her feet, kisses her, and then lies down on the ground. When she sees that he is asleep, she leaves him. Immediately a man comes in, takes off the King's crown, kisses it, and pours poison in the King's ear. He then goes out. The Queen returns, finds the King dead and appears distraught. The poisoner comes in again with two or three more people who mourn with her. The dead body is carried away and the poisoner woos the Queen with gifts: at first she seems reluctant, but in the end she accepts him. Then they go out*]

Ophelia What does it mean, my lord?

Hamlet It means mischief!

Ophelia Perhaps it's the plot of the play.

[*An **Actor** comes in to speak the Prologue*]

Hamlet We'll find out from this fellow. Actors can never keep a secret, they blurt out everything!

Actor For us and for our tragedy
We beg your hearing patiently. [*He goes out*]

Hamlet Was that little jingle meant to be a prologue?

* We must assume that the King and Queen do not pay attention while the Mime is being performed, so they are not aware of the subject of the play.

Ophelia It was certainly short, my lord.

Hamlet As a woman's love!

[*Actor King and Actor Queen come in*]

Actor King Across the sky has gone the golden sphere
        Sufficient times to make up thirty year
        Since love our hearts, and marriage did our hands,
        In mutual trust unite, with sacred bands.

Actor Queen As many journeys may the golden sun
        Perform again, before our love is done.
        But woe, alas! You've looked so ill of late,
        So much unlike your former cheerful state.
        But do not let my fears discomfort you:
        When a woman's love is great, her fears are too.

Actor King Oh, I must leave you soon, my dearest love,
        My limbs have almost lost the power to move!
        But you'll live on with honour, and will find
        A husband just as good—

Actor Queen   —You surely jest!
        Such love would be like treason in my breast.
        If I should wed again, let me be cursed:
        Second husbands are for those who've killed their first!

Hamlet A bitter pill…

Actor King Though I believe you mean the words you've spoken,
        The promises we make are often broken.
        How easily good intentions are mislaid!
        The debts we owe ourselves are seldom paid.
        The passion over, joy and grief both fade,
        And with them all the promises we made.
        Since life is not forever, is it strange
        That even love should with our fortunes change?
        When great men fall, their closest friends will leave;
        When poor men climb, they'll have no enemies.
        Now I will neatly end where I began:
        We think we choose, but Fate decrees the plan.
        You swear you won't a second husband wed;
        Such thoughts will die when your first lord is dead!

Actor Queen May earth deny me food, and heaven light;
        May joy and rest desert me day and night;

> Oh, may I live a life of endless pain
> If, widowed, I become a wife again!

Hamlet If she should break her word now!

Actor King A solemn oath! Now leave me please, my dear,
> I'll spend the afternoon just lying here,
> And have a pleasant sleep.

Actor Queen   Sleep softly, do.
> May trouble never come between us two.

[*The **Actor Queen** goes out and the **Actor King** lies down and goes to sleep*]

Hamlet [*To the Queen*] Do you like this play, Madam?

Queen I find the lady's promises rather extravagant!

Hamlet But I'm sure she'll keep them.

King [*To Polonius*] Do you know the story? Is there anything offensive in it?

Hamlet No, no, they are only *playing* at poisoning.

King What do they call the play?

Hamlet "The Mousetrap", figuratively speaking of course. It shows a murder done in Vienna. The King's name is Gonzago, his wife Baptista. You'll soon see. It's a wicked piece of work, but what of that? We have nothing to fear, leave that to the guilty! [***Actor Lucianus** comes in carrying a small bottle of poison*] This is Lucianus, the King's nephew.

Ophelia You make a good commentator, my lord.

Hamlet I can provide the words, if you and your lover make the movements.

Ophelia You have a bitter tongue, my lord.

Hamlet I could be sweet to you, but then you might end up with a full belly! [*To **Actor Lucianus***] Stop making those faces, and begin! Come on, murderer! "The croaking raven bellows for revenge..."

Actor Lucianus Black thoughts, skilled hands, the drug, the proper time,
> All these in secret session join, combine.
> You—evil essence, distilled so magically—
> Will end this healthy life immediately!

[*He holds up the bottle then pours poison in **Actor King**'s ear*]

Hamlet He poisons him in the garden, to get the throne. His name is Gonzago. It's a well-known story, written in the finest Italian. You'll soon see how the murderer gets Gonzago's wife.

Ophelia The King's got up.

Hamlet What? Frightened by shadows?

Queen [*To the King*] Are you all right, my lord?

Polonius Stop the play! [*To the Actors*] Be off with you!

King Lights! Lights!

[*The lights come on and they all go out except **Hamlet** and **Horatio***]

Hamlet Well, let the wounded deer go weep
                    While innocent creatures play.
             For some must watch while others sleep,
                    So runs the world away.
  [*Gaily*] If my luck should run out, wouldn't all this, together with a few feathers and flowers, get me a job with a bunch of actors?

Horatio A part-time job, perhaps!

Hamlet Well, Horatio, I'll bet a thousand pounds that the ghost is right. Did you see?

Horatio I certainly did, my lord.

Hamlet When they talked of poisoning...?

Horatio Yes, I noticed!

Hamlet If the King doesn't like it
        He'll just have to lump it!
  [***Rosencrantz** and **Guildenstern** come in*] Let's have some music! Fetch the musicians!

[***Rosencrantz** goes out, and comes in again a few moments later*]

Guildenstern May I have a word with you, my lord?

Hamlet A whole book, for all I care!

Guildenstern The King, sir—

Hamlet What about him, sir?

Guildenstern —has gone to his room, and is in a terrible state.

Hamlet Is he drunk, sir?

Guildenstern No, my lord, he's angry. And the Queen your mother is very upset, and has sent me to you—

Hamlet [*Bowing*] You are welcome!

Guildenstern My dear sir, that's not the point! If you're prepared to give a sensible answer, I'll do what your mother has asked. If not, you must excuse me.

Hamlet Sir, I cannot.

Guildenstern Cannot what, my lord?

Hamlet Give you a sensible answer. My brain's gone soft. But I will give you, or rather give my mother, as good an answer as I can. So, to the point. My mother, you say...

Rosencrantz She is astonished by your behaviour, quite bewildered!

Hamlet What a wonderful son, to be able to cause a mother such astonishment! Something significant must surely follow such maternal bewilderment? Proceed!

Rosencrantz She wishes to speak to you in her room, before you go to bed.

Hamlet If she were our mother ten times over, we'd obey her. Have you any more business with us?

Rosencrantz My lord, we were friends once.

Hamlet And I swear—by the devil—that we still are!

Rosencrantz My lord, why are you in such a bad mood? Your depression will get the better of you if you don't open up to your friends.

Hamlet I feel frustrated!

Rosencrantz How can you say that, when the King himself supports your succession to the throne?

Hamlet True, sir, but "The grass is greener..." You know the old proverb? [*The **Musicians** come in*] Ah, the recorders! Let me have one. [***Hamlet** takes it, and then takes **Guildenstern** aside*] What are you trying to do? Set a trap for me?

Guildenstern My lord, my duty impels me to be forward in my affection.

Hamlet What does that mean? [*He offers him the recorder*] Would you like to play this?

Guildenstern I don't know how to, my lord.

Hamlet Go on! [*Offering it to him*]

Guildenstern I don't know the fingering.

Hamlet Oh, it's as easy as lying. Cover these holes with your fingers and blow into it and it will play lovely music. Look!

Guildenstern But I can't get a decent sound out of it.

Hamlet And yet you think you can play *me*, sound my deepest feelings! What a worthless thing you must think I am! [***Polonius** comes in*] God bless you, sir!

Polonius My lord, the Queen would like to speak to you at once.

Hamlet [*Pointing to the audience*] Do you see that man out there? Don't you think he looks rather like a camel?

Polonius By God, you're right, sir!

Hamlet Actually, I think he's more like a weasel.

Polonius Yes, his nose is rather like a weasel's.

Hamlet Or a whale's?

Polonius Yes, yes, very like a whale's.

Hamlet In that case, I'll come to my mother straight away. [*To himself*] They treat me like an idiot! [*To **Polonius***] I'll be along soon. [***Polonius** goes out*] Leave me, friends. [*All the others go out*] Midnight! The witching time, when graves yawn and hell breathes out its evil! Now I could commit crimes too hideous for the light of day... [*He shudders*] I must go to my mother. I will be blunt with her, but not too cruel. I dare not let my deeds match my words, hypocrite that I am! My tongue, not my sword, shall be my weapon.

Scene 3

A room in the castle

| King |
| Rosencrantz |
| Guildenstern |
| Polonius |
| Hamlet |

[*The **King** comes in with **Rosencrantz** and **Guildenstern***]

King He worries me. I don't feel at all safe, in fact I feel quite threatened by his madness. You go and get yourselves ready and I'll see to the documents straight away. He must go with you to England.

Rosencrantz We'll get ourselves ready, your Majesty. The welfare of your subjects is a sacred duty.

Guildenstern Of course, individual citizens must look after themselves, but they have an even greater duty to look after the one on whose well-being they depend. When a king dies, everyone suffers. The king's sigh is the nation's groan.

King Get ready quickly, please. We must muzzle him.

[***Polonius** comes in as **Rosencrantz** and **Guildenstern** go out*]

Polonius My lord, he's going to his mother's room. I'll hide behind the curtains and listen. I've no doubt she'll give him a good talking to, and as you've so wisely said it's important that someone should hear what they say, since a mother is bound to be biased. Goodbye, your Majesty. I'll come and report to you before you go to bed.

King Thank you. [***Polonius** goes out*] Oh, how foul my crime is, it stinks to high heaven! It has the curse of Cain on it, a brother's murder! I long to pray, but guilt prevents me. But surely God's mercy can wash away the blood even of a brother's murder? And prayer is not just to keep us

35

from sin, but to save sinners? So I will pray. But what shall I say? "Dear God, please forgive my murder!" No, that's impossible. I still possess the things for which I did it: my ambition, the crown, the Queen! You can bribe the law and buy justice in this wicked world, but not in heaven. There's no trickery there, we must tell it all! What then? What can repentance do? What *can't* it do? But what if one *cannot* repent...? Oh, wretched, miserable soul...! The harder I struggle, the more trapped I feel. Angels above, help me! I must try to pray. I must repent. [*He kneels*] All may still be well.

[***Hamlet** comes in and sees the **King** on his knees*]

Hamlet [*To himself*] Now's my chance! I could do it so easily, while he's praying. I get my revenge, and he goes to heaven. [*He half draws his sword, then pauses*] To heaven! So a villain kills my father, and I, his only son, send him up to heaven! That's *reward*, not revenge. He killed my father before he had had time to confess his sins, and heaven alone knows what's happened to his soul. To kill this man while he is at prayer, his soul cleansed and ready for its Maker, is hardly revenge. No! I'll catch him when he's drunk or gambling, in some wicked act, nothing pure or holy, so that his soul will be damned and go headlong to hell! [*He sheathes his sword again*] My mother's waiting. [*Looking at the **King***] Your prayers can only postpone the evil day. [*He goes out*]

King Mere words without thoughts are useless. I cannot pray.

Scene 4

The Queen's private room

| Queen |
| Polonius |
| Hamlet |
| Ghost |

[*The **Queen** comes in with **Polonius***]

Polonius He'll be along soon. Don't mince your words. Tell him his pranks have become impossible, and that you've had to protect him from a great deal of anger and criticism. I'll hide over here. [*He goes to some curtains*] Please be firm with him.

Hamlet [*Off stage*] Mother, mother!

Queen I promise. Don't worry. Go on. I can hear him coming.

[***Polonius** hides behind the curtains. **Hamlet** comes in*]

Hamlet Now, mother, what's the matter?

Queen Hamlet, you've offended your father.

Hamlet Mother, *you've* offended *my* father.

Queen Come, come, that's a foolish thing to say!

Hamlet Go, go, that's a wicked reply!

Queen Hamlet! Have you forgotten who I am?

Hamlet No, by God, no! You are the Queen, your husband's brother's wife. And, however much I wish you weren't, you *are* my mother.

Queen [*Angrily, moving away*] There are people who can deal with you.

Hamlet Sit down! You shan't move until I have made you look into your very soul! [*He pushes her violently into a chair*]

Queen [*In a panic*] What are you doing? Are you going to murder me? Help! Help!

Polonius [*Behind the curtain*] Help! Help!

Hamlet [*Drawing his sword*] What's this? A rat? [*He plunges his sword through the curtain*] Dead for a dollar...!

Polonius Murder! [*He falls dead behind the curtain*]

Queen For pity's sake! What have you done?

Hamlet I don't know. Is it the King?

Queen You rash, you murderous, you—

Hamlet Murderous, yes! Almost as bad as killing a king and marrying his brother!

Queen Killing a king?

Hamlet Yes, lady, that's what I said. [*He lifts the curtain*] Polonius! You stupid, interfering fool, I mistook you for your master. Well, goodbye! Busybodies must take the consequences. [*To the **Queen***] Stop wringing your hands! Be quiet, sit down. I'll wring your heart instead, unless it's so brazen that nothing will touch it!

Queen How dare you speak to me like that! What have I done?

Hamlet Done? Haven't you made a mockery of marriage? Turned virtue into a hypocrite? Reduced religion to a mere string of words? Made love itself ashamed to show its innocent face?

Queen What makes you say such terrible things?

Hamlet [*He points to portraits of his father and his uncle*] Look at these: this... and this. Two brothers. Look at this one: the face of a god, full of grace and beauty. A proper man. This *was* your husband. Now look at this. This *is* your husband—a foul disease that's destroyed his brother. Have you no eyes? How could you leave this loveliness for this horror? You can't call it love. At your age, the passions should have grown cool. I know you still have feelings, but even the strongest passion retains some power to choose. What devil played blind man's buff with you?

Shame on you! If a woman of your age can't resist the foul hell of lust, what hope is there for youth with all its fire and passion!

Queen Oh Hamlet, stop! You have made me look into the very depths of my soul, and I see such evil there!

Hamlet ...wallowing in a stinking, sweaty bed, and making love like pigs!

Queen [*Putting her hands over her ears*] Don't! I can't bear it! Dear Hamlet, please stop!

Hamlet ...a slave not fit to lick his brother's boots, a thief who pocketed the crown and—

Queen Stop!

Hamlet ...a clown with a crown... [*The **Ghost** of Hamlet's father comes in. Only **Hamlet** can see and hear it*] Heaven help me! [*To the **Ghost***] What is it, my gracious lord?

Queen [*To herself*] He's mad, he's mad!

Hamlet You are angry with me for failing to carry out your commands. Am I right?

Ghost Remember! Yes, I have come to spur you on... But look how confused your mother is. Help her in her agony, the weak have strong imaginations. Speak to her, Hamlet!

Hamlet How are you, my lady?

Queen Ah, but how are *you*? Why are you staring into empty space, talking to thin air, with that wild look? Calm down, my dear. What are you looking at?

Hamlet At him, at him! How sad he looks! It's enough to melt a heart of stone. [*To the **Ghost***] Don't look at me in that pitiful way. You'll make me weep instead of avenging your murder.

Queen Who are you saying this to?

Hamlet Don't you see anything there?

Queen Nothing. But I can see all there is.

Hamlet Can't you hear anything either?

Queen No, just us talking.

Hamlet But look—there! Creeping away! My father, just as he was when he was alive. Look, going out of the door—now! [*The **Ghost** goes out*]

Queen You're imagining it! Madness can do this.

Hamlet Madness? My pulse is as steady as yours, I'm not mad. Test me: I can describe exactly what happened... Mother, for the love of God don't try to cover up your wickedness by pretending I'm mad. The evil will go on festering underneath. Confess, mother, repent! And try to avoid temptation in the future. Don't add to your sins... Forgive me for preaching like this. [*Bitterly*] Huh! What a sick age we live in when you have to apologise for doing good!

Queen Oh Hamlet, you have broken my heart!

Hamlet Throw away the worse part, and live a better life with the other. Good night! But whatever you do, don't go to my uncle's bed—at least pretend to be virtuous. Habit is a powerful thing, it can reinforce good actions as well as bad ones. Abstain tonight, and that will make it easier the next time, and the next... Once again, good night! And when you have prayed for God's blessing, I'll ask you for yours. As for this gentleman here [*pointing to **Polonius***] I am sorry I killed him, but heaven has punished me, and him through me. I'll dispose of his body and explain how he died. Good night again! I must be cruel in order to be kind. A bad enough beginning, this, but I fear worse is to come. [*He starts going, and then turns back*] One more thing!

Queen [*Weeping*] What shall I do?

Hamlet Not allow the bloated King to tempt you into bed again, to fondle your cheeks and call you his little mouse, and in return for a couple of slobbery kisses and filthy gropings to let on that I am not really mad but only pretending! That would be a fine thing! But how can one expect a lovely, modest, wise Queen like you to keep such intimate matters from a foul toad like him? [*Menacingly*] I warn you not to try any monkey tricks. You'll pay for it if you do!

Queen I swear I shan't breathe a word!

Hamlet I'm being sent to England. Did you know?

Queen Oh, my dear, I had forgotten. Yes, it's been decided.

Hamlet There are letters, written and sealed. And my two school-fellows, who I trust the way I trust poisonous snakes, are in charge and will no doubt set some trap for me. Never mind. It will be fun to get them to fall into the hole they've dug for me! I'll enjoy this confrontation. [*Referring to **Polonius***] This man will get me going. I'll lug his guts into the next room. This really *is* good night, mother! [*Looking at the body*] How solemn he looks now, how sensible and serious, when in his life he was nothing but a blabbering fool! Come, sir, let us draw to a conclusion. [*He drags the body out*]

ACT FOUR

King
Queen
(Rosencrantz)
(Guildenstern)

Scene 1

A room in the castle, late at night

[*The* **King**, *the* **Queen**, **Rosencrantz** *and* **Guildenstern** *come in*]

King [*To the* **Queen**] Something has upset you, you must tell me what it is. What's wrong? And where's your son?

Queen [*To* **Rosencrantz** *and* **Guildenstern**] Leave us for a moment. [*They go out*] My dear, you'll never believe what I've seen tonight.

King What is it, Gertrude? How is Hamlet?

Queen Quite out of his mind! He heard a movement behind the curtain in my room, whipped out his sword shouting "A rat, a rat!", and—in a mad fit—killed good old Polonius.

King No! And to think it could have been me! He's a threat to us all... And who will be held responsible? I will, for failing to restrain the mad young man. I've been too kind to him, allowed him to run out of control. Where is he?

Queen He's removing the body and weeping over it, full of compassion despite his madness.

King Come, Gertrude! I'll send him away at dawn, and face up to the horror of the situation as best I can. [*He calls*] Guildenstern! [**Rosencrantz** *and* **Guildenstern** *come in*] Friends, go and get some help. Hamlet's gone quite mad—he's killed Polonius and dragged him out of his mother's room. You must find him, but treat him kindly. And take the body into the chapel. Hurry, please! [*They go out*] Come, Gertrude, we'll discuss the whole situation with our advisers, put them in the picture. With luck, we'll escape criticism. Come along! All this has shaken me badly.

40

Scene 2
Another room in the castle, a little later

[*Hamlet* comes in. He has put *Polonius'* body in a cupboard]

Hamlet Safely hidden!

Rosencrantz & Guildenstern [*Off stage*] Hamlet! Lord Hamlet!

Hamlet What's that? Who's calling me? Ah, here they come.

[*Rosencrantz* and *Guildenstern* come in with some *Attendants*]

Rosencrantz My lord, what have you done with the body?

Hamlet Put it where it belongs, in the dust.

Rosencrantz Tell us where it is, so that we can take it to the chapel.

Hamlet Don't you believe it!

Rosencrantz Believe what?

Hamlet That I can keep *your* secrets, but not *mine*. Besides, how should the son of a King reply to a sponge?

Rosencrantz Are you calling me a sponge, my lord?

Hamlet Yes. You soak up everything the King has to offer: jobs, favours, money. But in the end the King gets good value. When he wants information, he squeezes you dry.

Rosencrantz My lord, you must tell us where the body is and go with us to the King.

Hamlet The body is in the kingdom, but the King isn't with the body. The King is a thing...

Guildenstern A thing, my lord?

Hamlet A nothing! Take me to him.

King
(Lords)
Rosencrantz
(Guildenstern)
Hamlet
(Attendants)

Scene 3
Another room in the castle, later still

[*The King* comes in with two or three *Lords*]

King I have told them to look for him and find the body. It's dangerous for him to remain free, but we mustn't come down too heavily on him. He is very popular with the mob, which tends to be swayed by appearances; they'll ignore his offence and only notice our punishment. To prevent trouble, his sudden removal must seem well considered. [*Rosencrantz comes in*] Well, what's happened?

Rosencrantz We can't get him to tell us where the body is, my lord, but he's waiting outside, under guard.

King Bring him in.

Rosencrantz [*Calls*] Bring in Lord Hamlet!

[**Guildenstern** *and some* **Attendants** *bring* **Hamlet** *in*]

King Now, Hamlet, where's Polonius?

Hamlet At supper.

King [*Puzzled*] At supper?

Hamlet Not eating, sir, but *being* eaten. A committee of crafty worms is at him. After all, they're the masters: we feed animals to feed ourselves, and feed ourselves to feed worms. The fat king and the thin beggar are just two different courses, that's all!

King Oh dear, oh dear!

Hamlet You can fish with a worm that's eaten a king, and then eat the fish.

King What do you mean?

Hamlet Just that a king can proceed through the guts of a beggar.

King Where is Polonius?

Hamlet In heaven. Send someone to see! If they don't find him there, look in the other place yourself. But if you haven't found him in a week or two, your nose will, as you go up the back stairs.

King [*To the* **Attendants**] Go and look for him.

Hamlet He won't run away! [*Some of the* **Attendants** *go out*]

King Hamlet, for your own safety, which concerns me as much as your crime does, we must send you away as quickly as possible. Everything is ready for you to sail to England.

Hamlet To England?

King Yes, Hamlet.

Hamlet Good!

King You'd think so, if you knew my reasons.

Hamlet I know a little bird that knows them! To England, then. Goodbye, dear mother!

King I'm your *father* Hamlet.

Hamlet [*Firmly*] *Mother*! Father and mother are man and wife; man and wife are one flesh; so, my *mother*. Now, to England! [*He goes out with the remaining* **Attendants**]

King [*To **Rosencrantz** and **Guildenstern***] Follow him, and get him aboard quickly. He must go before dawn. The papers are all sealed and ready, so please be quick. [*They all go out except the **King**, who speaks to himself*] King of England! If you value my friendship—as you should do after your recent defeat—you will obey my command to put Hamlet to death immediately. He's like a fever in my blood, that you must cure! I'll have no peace of mind until I know it's done.

Fortinbras	Hamlet
Officer	Rosencrantz
(2nd Officer)	(Guildenstern)
(Norwegian	(Attendants)
Soldiers)	

Scene 4

Denmark, near the border with Norway, later the same day

[***Fortinbras** comes in with two **Officers** and some **Norwegian Soldiers***]

Fortinbras [*To an **Officer***] Captain, take my greetings to the King of Denmark and inform him that I, Fortinbras, require an escort through his country, as he promised. If his Majesty wishes, I will meet him myself.

Officer Yes, sir.

Fortinbras [*To a second **Officer***] Carry on!

[*The **Soldiers** march off, followed by the second **Officer** and **Fortinbras**. As the first **Officer** is going out the other way he meets **Hamlet**, **Rosencrantz**, **Guildenstern** and some **Attendants** coming in*]

Hamlet What soldiers are those, Captain?

Officer Norwegian, sir.

Hamlet Where are they going? Who's in command?

Officer The Norwegian King's nephew, sir, young Fortinbras. They're going to Poland.

Hamlet Are you planning an invasion?

Officer Oh, no! All we're aiming for is a worthless piece of land, purely for its name. Personally, I wouldn't pay five pounds to farm it!

Hamlet Surely the Poles will never defend it?

Officer Oh yes, they've already got troops there, and now even two thousand men and twenty thousand pounds won't settle this stupid dispute.

Hamlet [*To himself*] This is how peace and prosperity, like a festering abcess, work their deadly corruption... Thank you, Captain.

Officer Thank you sir. [*He goes out*]

Rosencrantz Shall we go on, my lord?

Hamlet I'll be with you in a minute. You go on ahead. [*They all go out, leaving **Hamlet** on his own*] Time and again, events spur me to revenge! What is a man, if all he's interested in is eating and sleeping? A mere animal! Surely we haven't been blessed with such powers of reasoning and foresight simply to have them moulder away unused... I have the motive, the will, the strength and the means to do it, so why do I still stand here talking about it? Is it forgetfulness, or caution—or just plain cowardice? I even have the example of this sensitive, spirited young Prince, commanding a vast army and defying danger and death. There's greatness for you! Not waiting for a noble cause but, where honour is in question, being prepared to fight for a mere trifle. And yet look at me, with a father murdered and a mother dishonoured, doing absolutely nothing; just shamefacedly watching twenty thousand men go to their deaths for a miserable plot of land not large enough to be their graveyard! From now on, it must be blood or nothing!

Queen	(Attendants)
Horatio	Messenger
Gentleman	Laertes
Ophelia	(Danish
King	Soldiers)

Scene 5

A room in the castle, some days later

[*The **Queen**, **Horatio** and a **Gentleman** come in*]

Queen I will not speak to her.

Gentleman She's in a desperate state, she deserves sympathy. *

Queen What does she want?

Gentleman She keeps talking about her father, says the world's not to be trusted, and tears her hair, and flares up at the slightest provocation. Her words seem to make some sort of sense, but it's really all nonsense. Though people do read things into her words, which her nods and winks and gestures seem to confirm, but you can't be sure. They could cause trouble. *

Horatio It would be a good idea to talk to her, to discourage dangerous gossip.

Queen Let her come in, then. [*The **Gentleman** goes out. She speaks to herself*] My guilty soul sees danger in every little thing. [*She sighs*] The more guilt tries to hide, the more it betrays itself.

* These speeches are sometimes given to Horatio.

[*Ophelia comes in*]

Ophelia Where is Denmark's lovely Queen?

Queen How are you, Ophelia?

Ophelia [*Sings*] How shall I know if my love is true?
           By his pilgrim staff and his worn out shoe!

Queen What do you mean, my dear?

Ophelia Did you speak? Listen to this!
      [*Sings*] He is dead and gone, lady,
           He is dead and gone;
        At his head, a grass green turf,
           At his feet, a stone.   [*She sighs deeply*]

[*The* **King** *comes in with some* **Attendants** *while she is singing*]

King How are you, my dear?

Ophelia Well, thank you. They say the owl was a baker's daughter. We know what we are, but not what we may become. God be at your table!

King [*To the* **Queen**] She's thinking about her father—

Ophelia No discussion, please, but when they ask what it means, say
      [*Sings*] Tomorrow is Saint Valentine's day,
          "I'll be your sweet young bride."
        Then the young man said, "Come to my bed",
          And so her innocence died.

King Pretty Ophelia—

Ophelia No, I'll finish it off, without swearing.
      [*Sings*] Young men will do it when they want—
          By Cock, they are to blame!

King How long has she been like this?

Ophelia I hope all will be well. We must be patient. But I can't help crying when I think of them laying him in the cold ground. My brother shall be told. Thank you for your good advice... Bring my coach! Good night, ladies, good night. Sweet ladies, good night, good night! [*She goes out*]

King [*To* **Horatio**] Follow her. Watch her carefully, please. [**Horatio** *goes out*] This comes from her desperate grief at her father's death. Oh Gertrude, Gertrude! Sorrows never come singly! First, her father killed; then your son gone, a victim of his own violence. The people are muttering and whispering about Polonius' death, and we were stupid enough to bury him secretly. And now poor Ophelia has lost her reason. And to cap it all, her brother Laertes comes over secretly from France, wonders what's going on, and laps up all these vicious rumours about his father's death, of which I'm accused for lack of other evidence. Dear Gertrude, this is like dying a thousand times! [*Shouts are heard off stage*]

Queen What's that?

King [*To the Attendants*] Tell them to guard the door! [*A Messenger comes in*]

Messenger Quick, my lord! Laertes has come charging in at the head of a wild rabble, and he's overwhelmed your Officers. The mob are calling him "Lord Laertes". They've got short memories and seem to have forgotten all their old ways. They are calling for Laertes to be King.

Queen They are like a pack of dogs on a false trail!

[*The sound of a door being broken down is heard*]

King They're breaking in!

Laertes [*Shouting off stage*] Where's the King? [*He comes in with some Danish Soldiers, to whom he gives orders*] Guard the entrance! [*The Soldiers go out, and Laertes speaks angrily to the King*] You villain! What's happened to my father?

Queen [*Holding him*] Calm down, Laertes!

Laertes [*Furiously*] What? Betray my father and dishonour my mother?

King Why are you in such a rage, Laertes? [*To the Queen*] Let him go, Gertrude! I'm safe. God will always protect a king from treason. [*To Laertes*] Why are you so angry? [*To the Queen*] Let him go! [*To Laertes*] Speak, man!

Laertes Where is my father?

King He's dead.

Queen [*Anxiously, indicating the King*] But he's not to blame!

King [*To the Queen*] Let him ask what he wants!

Laertes How did he die? No tricks, now. To hell with loyalty! I'm prepared to swear by the devil himself and dare damnation! I'll do anything to avenge my father's death!

King So, Laertes, you want to know who killed your father. Will you take your revenge on whoever it turns out to be, friend or foe?

Laertes They're *all* his enemies!

King Do you want to know who they are, then?

Laertes I'll welcome his friends with open arms.

King Well said! It'll soon be quite obvious to you that I am entirely innocent

46

of your father's death, and truly sorry about it. [*Ophelia is heard singing off stage. The **King** calls to the **Soldiers***] Let her come in!

Laertes What's going on? [*Ophelia comes in, looking distraught*] I don't believe this... I can't bear to look... [*Fiercely*] Someone will pay for this! [*Gently*] Dear sister; sweet, innocent Ophelia! Can a young girl's mind be as vulnerable as an old man's life? Has love robbed her of her senses?

Ophelia [*Sings*] They laid him down in his cold bed,
> And on his grave their tears they shed.

Goodbye, my dove.

Laertes This moves me to revenge far more than reason ever could.

Ophelia You must sing "A-down a-down..." How well it fits! And the dishonest steward stole his master's daughter...

Laertes There's such meaning in this nonsense!

Ophelia [*To **Laertes***] Here's rosemary for you, for remembrance; and here are pansies, for sorrow. [*To the **King***] Here's fennel for you, and columbine. [*To the **Queen***] Here's rue for you, and some for me; it's called herb-of-grace on Sundays. It's different for you. [*As if to **Hamlet***] And here's a daisy. I would have given you some violets, but they withered when my father died. They say he died well. [*She sings*] "For bonny sweet Robin is all my joy."

Laertes Sadness, suffering, sorrow—even hell!—she makes it all sound so pretty, so charming.

Ophelia [*Sings*] Will he not come again?
> No, he is dead
> He will never come again.
> His beard was like snow,
> He is gone, he is gone.
> God have mercy on his soul!

And on all Christian souls. God bless you! [*She goes out*]

King Laertes, you must let me share your grief. Choose your wisest friends, let them judge, and if they find me guilty in any way, I'll give you my crown, my kingdom, my life, everything I possess! If not, be patient, and we will work together to satisfy your honour.

Laertes Very well. But how he died, and the way he was buried without honour or ceremony, I demand it all be made public!

King It shall be. And the offender will be punished, whoever he is. Come with me!

| Horatio |
| Servant |
| Sailor |
| (Sailors) |

Scene 6
Another room in the castle

[***Horatio*** *comes in with a* ***Servant***]

Horatio Who wants to see me?

Servant Some sailors, sir. They say they've got some letters for you.

Horatio Tell them to come in. [*The* ***Servant*** *goes out*] Now, who on earth could they be from, other than Prince Hamlet?

[*Some* ***Sailors*** *come in*]

Sailor Good morning, sir. Is your name Horatio? [***Horatio*** *nods, and he gives him a letter*] It's from the ambassador who was on his way to England.

Horatio [*He reads* ***Hamlet's*** *letter aloud*] "Horatio, when you have read this, send these sailors to the King; they have letters for him. Two days after we set sail, a well-armed pirate ship chased us and caught us up. We were forced to fight, and during the struggle I boarded the pirate ship. It immediately got away and I became their prisoner, but they treated me well, knowing that I could be of use to them. Give the King these letters, and then come to me post-haste, as if the devil himself were after you! My news will astound you! These men will bring you to me. Rosencrantz and Guildenstern are still on their way to England; I have much to tell you about them. Yours, Hamlet." [*To the* ***Sailors***] Come along, I'll show you where to take those letters, then you can take me to the man who gave them to you.

| King |
| Laertes |
| Messenger |
| Queen |

Scene 7
The King's private room

[*The* ***King*** *and* ***Laertes*** *come in*]

King So now you *know* I'm innocent, and you must look on me as your friend, since you've understood so clearly that the man who killed your father was after me too.

Laertes So it would appear. But tell me, why did you do nothing about these terrible crimes when you were so concerned about your own well-being and safety?

King For two special reasons, which may seem slight to you, but are important to me. The Queen his mother dotes on him, and whether I like it or not, I cannot live without her. My second reason is his popularity. He is held in such affection by the ordinary people that they would have made a martyr of him, and my accusations would have rebounded on me.

Laertes So, I have lost a noble father, and my sister, who was perfection itself, has been driven mad. But I'll get my revenge!

King Of course you will! And don't for a moment imagine that I'll take such insults lightly. You'll hear more soon. My affection for your father, as well as my concern for myself, should make you realise— [*A Messenger comes in with some letters*] What is it?

Messenger Letters from Hamlet, my lord. These are for your Majesty, and this is for the Queen.

King From Hamlet? Who brought them?

Messenger Some sailors, my lord.

King Laertes, stay and listen. [*To the Messenger*] Go now. [*He goes out, and the King reads*] "High and Mighty, I have been thrown up destitute on your shores. Tomorrow I should be obliged if you would grant me an audience so that, with your permission, I can tell you the reason for my strange and sudden return. Hamlet." What can this mean? Have the others come back? Or is it some sort of trick?

Laertes Do you recognise the writing?

King Yes, it's Hamlet's. "Destitute", and he's added "alone". Can you explain it?

Laertes I'm lost, my lord. But let him come! I long to tell him to his face "This is how you'll die!"

King If it's true—though I don't see how it can be... but it must be—are you prepared to follow my advice?

Laertes Yes, my lord, as long as you don't recommend peace!

King Peace of mind! Now, if he *is* back, and doesn't intend to go on with his journey, I'll devise a scheme that he *can't* escape from. And no one will be blamed for his death; even his mother will think it was an accident.

Laertes Very good, my lord. Especially if I can be the one to carry it out.

King That's good. [*He pauses*] Laertes, since you went abroad, people have been talking about you, about a particular skill of yours. Hamlet's heard about it, and it's the thing he envies most in you, though I must say I consider it quite unimportant.

Laertes What skill is that, my lord?

King A rather trivial one, perhaps, but a good one for young people like you. Two months ago, a gentleman from Normandy was here. I've seen some excellent horsemen in my time in France, but not one to touch him. I've never seen anything like it. He seemed to grow out of his horse!

Laertes A Norman, you say?

King That's right.

Laertes It must be Lamord. I know him well. He's brilliant!

King He gave a glowing report of your skill as a swordsman, especially with the rapier, and said there wasn't a Frenchman who could match you. All this made Hamlet so jealous that he could hardly wait to challenge you. Now... [*Pause*]

Laertes Yes, my lord?

King Laertes, was your father really dear to you?

Laertes [*Suspiciously*] What do you mean?

King Oh, I'm not saying you never loved him, but I've noticed that just as love needs time to grow, it is bound by its very nature to fade. It can even destroy itself by its own intensity. So we must act, not allow ourselves to be diverted. That's the way to avoid useless regrets. Now, to the heart of the matter. Hamlet is coming back. How would you show, and not just by words, that you are your father's son?

Laertes I'd cut his throat, even in a church!

King That's the spirit! There should be no safe haven for a murderer! Listen, Laertes. I'd like you to keep to your room. When Hamlet returns, he'll be told you're here, and we'll make sure your skill is well publicised. Then we'll bring the two of you together, with a wager on the match. Hamlet won't bother to examine the foils, he's far too trusting and straightforward, so you can contrive to choose an unguarded one, and use the contest to avenge your father's death.

Laertes I'll do it! And I have in my possession some poison that's so lethal that the merest drop will be enough to kill him. I'll put it on my sword.

King We must consider the details carefully. We can't afford to fail and be caught out, so it's important to have a second plan in reserve. Let me see, we'll bet on your skill... I know! Fight really hard, so you'll both get hot and thirsty, and when he asks for a drink, I'll have one ready which will do the trick even if he escapes your poison. [*The **Queen** comes in*] What is it, Gertrude?

Queen Troubles come thick and fast. Laertes, your sister's drowned!

Laertes Drowned? Where? How?

Queen There's a weeping willow that grows beside a stream, its silvery leaves reflected in the clear waters. Your sister came there with fantastic garlands made from buttercups and nettles, daises and orchises, which some call "dead men's fingers". While she was reaching out to hang up her garland of wild flowers, a treacherous branch broke and plunged her and her flowers into the flowing stream. For a while she lay there, held up by her clothes, singing snatches of old tunes, as if the water were her element, quite unaware of the danger she was in. But soon her sodden clothes pulled her down to her death.

Laertes So she's drowned... You've had water enough, poor Ophelia, you don't need my tears! And yet I can't stop myself... [*He weeps*] But why should I be ashamed? There'll be no more weakness after this. Goodbye, my lord. Oh, I'd be so angry, if I wasn't so... [*He goes out sobbing*]

King Let's follow him, Gertrude. I've had such trouble calming him down, and now this! Come!

ACT FIVE

1st Gravedigger	Laertes
2nd Gravedigger	Priest
Hamlet	(Lords)
Horatio	(Attendants)
King	(Ophelia's
Queen	corpse)

Scene 1

A churchyard in Elsinore

[*Two* **Gravediggers** *come in carrying spades and other tools*]

1st Gravedigger But why is she having a Christian burial, when she's done it on purpose?

2nd Gravedigger That's how it is, so let's get on with it. The crowner has sat on her case and says she must have a Christian burial.

1st Gravedigger But why? Unless she drowned herself in her own defence.

2nd Gravedigger That's what they say.

1st Gravedigger It must be what the lawyers call "self offence", then. Let me explain. [*He draws in the dust*] Here's the water, right? And here's the man. Now, if the man goes into the water and drowns himself, willy-nilly, he drowns himself. See? But if the water comes to the man and drowns him, you can't say he drowned hisself, can you? Consequentially, if you're not guilty of causing your own death, you can't be said to shorten your own life.

2nd Gravedigger Shall I tell you the truth? If she hadn't been a great Lady they wouldn't have given her a Christian burial.

1st Gravedigger You're right there. And I call it a real shame that these high-ups should have the privilege of drowning or hanging theirselves when ordinary Christians aren't allowed to. [*He starts digging*] We follow Adam's profession, us gardeners and gravediggers. We're gentlemen.

2nd Gravedigger Was Adam a gentleman, then?

1st Gravedigger He was the first to have a coat of arms.

2nd Gravedigger He never did!

1st Gravedigger Don't you understand the Bible? It says there that Adam digged. How could he dig without arms?

2nd Gravedigger Get away with you! [*They dig*]

1st Gravedigger Who builds something stronger than either a house-builder, a carpenter or a shipbuilder?

2nd Gravedigger Ah! The gallows-maker, because his contraption can outlive a thousand customers!

1st Gravedigger The "gallows-maker"! That's quite good, that is. But what makes it good? It's good for bad people, consequentially you're a bad'un for saying the gallows is stronger than the church! Have another go!

2nd Gravedigger I've got it! [*Pause. He scratches his head*] Christ! I've forgotten.

[***Hamlet** comes in with **Horatio**. They pause at the side of the stage*]

1st Gravedigger Well, don't punish yourself. Hitting a silly ass won't make it go any faster. And when you're asked again, just say "a gravedigger". The houses that *he* makes last till doomsday. Go and fetch me a mug of beer! [*The **2nd Gravedigger** goes out. The **1st Gravedigger** digs and sings*]   In youth, when I did love, did love,
I thought it was so sweet
To clutch and squeeze my very own...

Hamlet How can this fellow bear to sing while digging a grave? Hasn't he got any feelings?

Horatio Perhaps habit has blunted them.

Hamlet Yes. Only the rich can afford feelings.

1st Gravedigger [*Sings*] But age crept up with stealthy steps,
And clawed me in his clutch.

[*He throws a skull out of the grave*]

Hamlet That skull had a tongue in it and could sing once, and he throws it down as if it belonged to Cain, the very first murderer! It might have been a politician, some fellow who was clever enough to outwit God—and now this idiot has outwitted him!

Horatio Yes, my lord.

1st Gravedigger [*Sings*] A pickaxe, a shovel, a spade,
A fine deep grave have made.

[*He throws another skull out*]

Hamlet [*Pointing to the skull*] And that might have been a lawyer! Where are his whys and wherefores now, his pros and his cons and all the other tricks of his trade? And why doesn't he sue this crazy fellow for assault? Or think of it, he might have been a great landlord in his time, busy with rents and rebates, fees and fines. A fine fee he's got for his pains: a head full of dirt! Even the title deeds of his lands couldn't fit in there [*pointing to the grave*] but it's all the space he can call his own. [*To the Gravedigger*] Whose grave is that?

1st Gravedigger Mine sir.

Hamlet I mean, what man are you digging it for?

1st Gravedigger No man, sir.

Hamlet What woman, then?

1st Gravedigger No woman, neither.

Hamlet Who's going to be buried in it?

1st Gravedigger Someone who was a woman, sir, but—God rest her soul!—she's dead.

Hamlet [*To Horatio*] You have to pick your words carefully these days, the peasants have become so sophisticated. [*To the Gravedigger*] How long have you been a gravedigger?

1st Gravedigger I started the day our last King Hamlet defeated Fortinbras.

Hamlet How long ago was that?

1st Gravedigger Any fool knows that! It was the day young Hamlet was born, the one who's mad and has been sent to England.

Hamlet Why has he been sent to England?

1st Gravedigger Because he's mad, and they hope he'll come to his senses. Anyway, if he doesn't it won't much matter. They're all mad there, so no one will notice.

Hamlet How did he go mad?

1st Gravedigger Oh, in a very odd way. By losing his wits!

Hamlet How long does it take for a body to rot in the earth?

1st Gravedigger Well, so long as it's not rotten before it dies, which many are nowadays, a body should last you some eight or nine years. Now, here's a skull that's been in the earth for twenty-three years.

Hamlet Whose was it?

1st Gravedigger A crazy fellow, he was. Who do you think?

Hamlet I don't know.

1st Gravedigger Curse his high spirits! He poured a bottle of whisky over me head once... This, sir, was Yorick's skull, the King's jester.

Hamlet Let me see. [*He takes the skull*] Alas, poor Yorick! I knew him, Horatio. He used to be so full of jokes, always bubbling with ideas. I remember how he used to carry me around on his back. Here were the lips that I used to kiss... Ugh! The very thought turns my stomach over! Where are your jokes now? Your dances, your songs? Your wit that used to set the table roaring with laughter? Quite crestfallen, eh? Go to my Lady's chamber and tell her that however much she paints her face, she'll come to this in the end! See if you can make her laugh at that...! Tell me something, Horatio.

Horatio What's that, my lord?

Hamlet Do you think Alexander the Great looked like this in his grave?

Horatio No doubt about it.

Hamlet And smelt like this? Ugh! How low we fall, Horatio! Just imagine, Alexander's noble remains bunging up a beer barrel!

> Great Caesar dead and turned to clay
> Now fills a hole to keep the cold away!

[*He looks off stage*] Sh! Here comes the King. [**Hamlet** *and* **Horatio** *go to the side of the stage as a procession comes in.* **Ophelia**'s *corpse is carried in by Attendants, followed by the* **King** *and* **Queen**, **Laertes**, **Lords** *and a* **Priest**] And the Queen. Whose funeral is it? And with so little ceremony... It's obviously someone important, but he must have taken his own life. Let's watch them.

Laertes [*To the* **Priest**] Is that all?

Hamlet [*To* **Horatio**] That's Laertes, a fine young man. Listen!

Priest We have performed all the rites that we have permission for. If the King had not overruled the Church, the manner of her death would have denied her burial in consecrated ground, and her coffin would have been pelted with stones. But as it is, she's been allowed garlands and flowers and the bell has tolled for her.

Laertes [*Incredulously*] Nothing more?

Priest Nothing more! It would be wrong to pray for her in the way we do for souls that have departed in peace.

Laertes Put her in her grave, [**Ophelia**'s *body is lowered into the grave*] and from her pure and lovely body may sweet violets grow! [*To the* **Priest**, *furiously*] My sister will be an angel in heaven when you are howling in hell, you pathetic priest!

Hamlet What? Sweet Ophelia?

Queen [*Scattering flowers into the grave*] Sweet flowers for a sweet young maid. Farewell! I hoped you would have been my Hamlet's wife, and that these flowers would have adorned your marriage bed, not your grave.

Laertes [*As earth is thrown into the grave*] A thousand curses on the murderer who drove you mad! Stop! I'll hold her in my arms one last time! [*He jumps into the grave*] Now you can pile your earth on the living as well as the dead; pile it up as high as Everest!

Hamlet [*Coming forward*] What right have you to talk in that way? I am Hamlet the Dane! [*He jumps into the grave*]

Laertes [*To **Hamlet***] The devil take your soul!

Hamlet What kind of a prayer is that? [***Laertes** grabs **Hamlet** by the throat*] Take your hands off me! I'm not easily roused, but you'd better be careful. Keep your hands off me! [*They fight*]

King Get them apart!

Queen Hamlet! Hamlet!

[***Horatio** and some of the **Attendants** separate them and they come out of the grave*]

Hamlet I'll fight him to the finish for this!

Queen My son, what's the matter?

Hamlet I loved Ophelia! Forty thousand brothers with all their love couldn't have loved her more. [*To **Laertes***] What will you do for her?

King [*To **Laertes***] He's mad, Laertes.

Hamlet [*To **Laertes***] Weep? Fight? Tear yourself apart? Eat a crocodile? Then I'll do the same. Have you come here to whine? To show me up by jumping into her grave? Go on, be buried alive with her, and I'll do it too. You babble about mountains, but I say pile up the earth till it reaches the sun! Huh! I can boast as well as you!

Queen His madness will rage for a while, but he'll soon calm down.

Hamlet [*To **Laertes***] Listen! Why are you treating me like this? I've always liked you... [***Laertes** does not reply*] Oh never mind! Anyway, what does it all matter? Cats will miaow, and dogs will have their day. [*He goes out*]

King [*To **Horatio***] Please keep an eye on him, Horatio. [***Horatio** goes out. To **Laertes***] Be patient, and remember what I said last night. I'll press ahead with our plan. [*To the **Queen***] Keep a close watch on your son. [*To everyone*] This grave shall have a lasting memorial. We shall have peace soon, but in the meantime we must all be patient.

Hamlet	Laertes
Horatio	(Lords)
Osric	(Attendants)
A Lord	Fortinbras
King	English Ambassadors
Queen	Norwegian Soldiers

Scene 2
The Great Hall in the castle

[*Hamlet* and *Horatio* come in]

Hamlet [*He is holding a letter*] That's enough of that! Now for this one. You remember the circumstances?

Horatio Of course, my lord.

Hamlet I couldn't sleep for worrying, I was in agony. Then a lucky impulse, which is often better than careful planning, and shows that providence can guide us despite ourselves...

Horatio That's true.

Hamlet On an impulse, I groped my way in the dark to their cabin, found the package, and went back to my room. I was so scared, Horatio, that I threw caution to the winds an unsealed the royal document. In it I found strict orders that I was to be killed immediately, without delay, without so much as waiting for the axe to be sharpened! What royal trickery! A whole host of reasons was given, such as "the safety of Denmark", and of England too, making me out to be a diabolical source of danger.

Horatio It's incredible!

Hamlet Here it is. Read it when you have time. [*He gives him the letter*] Do you want to know what happened next?

Horatio Please!

Hamlet I was in terrible danger, but—with my brain performing well—I sat down and invented a whole new set of orders, and wrote them out neatly. That's a skill I once learned and it served me well, though I used to despise good handwriting as much as any doctor! I wrote out an order from the Danish King to the English King pointing out that "as England is subject to the Dane", "as Love must grow and blossom between them", "as Peace should flourish", and many other fine "as's", he must put the bringers of this letter to death without delay, with no questions asked and without even allowing them time for confession.

Horatio How did you seal it?

Hamlet By great good fortune I had my father's signet ring in my purse, so I sealed the letter and put it back in their cabin without anyone noticing. You know the rest.

Horatio So that's the end of Rosencrantz and Guildenstern!

Hamlet They had only themselves to blame. My conscience is clear. They were more than willing agents, after all. Common folk shouldn't get in the way when their betters are fighting

Horatio What sort of a king is this!

Hamlet Don't you think it's my duty—he killed my father, seduced my mother, ruined all my hopes and even plotted to murder me—aren't I duty bound to take my revenge? Wouldn't the sin be to let this corruption spread?

Horatio It won't be long before he knows what's happened in England.

Hamlet Not long, but time enough for me... I'm sorry I lost my temper with Laertes, Horatio. I can appreciate how he feels, I'll make it up with him. But his showing off did make me very angry.

Horatio [*He sees someone coming*] Good lord, who's this?

[***Osric** comes in. He is dressed very fashionably, he is wearing a hat, and he keeps on bowing. He speaks in a very affected way*]

Osric Your Lordship is most welcome back to Denmark.

Hamlet Thank you sir, thank you. [*To **Horatio**, quietly*] Do you know this butterfly?

Horatio [*Quietly, to **Hamlet**]* No, my lord.

Hamlet [*To **Horatio**]* You're lucky! He's a big landowner, and when you're lord of the beasts you can dine with the King!

Osric My dear sir, if your lordship were at leisure to receive it, I could convey a message from the King. [*He takes his hat off and uses it as a fan*]

Hamlet I will give it my fullest attention, sir... Your hat's meant for your head!

Osric Thank you, my lord, but it's very hot. The King has bet—

Hamlet No, I'd say it was cold. The wind is from the north.

Osric You're right, my lord... well, I don't know... [*He puts his hat on*] We have here, newly arrived at court, Laertes, an absolutely gentlemanly gentleman, positively overflowing with distinction and good manners. The very model of a gentleman. [*He takes his hat off again*]

Hamlet [*Holding up a warning finger*] Remember! [***Osric** puts his hat on again*] Sir, your descriptive skill does him no injustice. I know very well that the catalogue of his accomplishments defies memorisation and his rarity is such as to deny comparison.

Osric Your lordship's words are indescribably apt.

Hamlet The relevancy? [*Pause*] Why does this gentleman enter our humble speech?

Osric [*He doesn't understand*] Sir?

Hamlet What is the signification of naming him?

Osric Who? Laertes?

Horatio [*To **Hamlet**, quietly*] You've squeezed him dry—he's run out of juicy words!

Hamlet Yes, him, sir.

Osric I know you know how excellent Laertes is—

Hamlet Oh, I wouldn't say that. Only the excellent can appreciate excellence. To know another we need to know ourselves.

Osric I mean, excellent with his weapon. His reputation among his peers is unmatchable.

Hamlet What *is* his weapon?

Osric Rapier and dagger.

Hamlet That's two, but never mind.

Osric The King has wagered six very fine horses, sir, against six French rapiers, with belts and buckles. Three of the accoutrements are fabulous!

Hamlet What do you mean, "accoutrements"?

Horatio [*To **Hamlet***] I knew you'd need a footnote!

Osric The fittings, sir.

Hamlet And why are they "wagered", as you call it?

Osric The King has wagered that out of twelve rounds, Laertes won't win more than eight. It could be arranged now, if your lordship is ready.

Hamlet I'll be here in the Hall. I'm free now. If the swords are brought out, and the gentleman is willing, and the King wants it, I'll try and win. Otherwise, all I'll suffer will be some damage to my reputation and the odd hit.

Osric Shall I report you to that effect, sir?

Hamlet Yes, dress it up as you wish.

Osric I can assure your lordship of my service at all times, sir. [*He goes out, bowing*]

Hamlet I'm sure no one else can!

Horatio He learnt to bow before he was born!

Hamlet And I'll bet he bowed to the breast before sucking! There are plenty like him; they mouth the words but miss the meaning—all froth and bubble!

[*A **Lord** comes in*]

Lord My lord, the King and Queen and the others are coming down. The Queen would like you to have a friendly word with Laertes before you begin.

Hamlet She's quite right. [*The **Lord** goes out*]

Horatio You'll lose, my lord.

Hamlet I don't think so. I've been practising hard ever since Laertes went to France. I'll win four out of the twelve. And yet you wouldn't believe how uneasy I feel... [*He puts his hand to his heart and sighs*] But never mind.

Horatio No, my lord—

Hamlet It's nothing. Woman's stuff!

Horatio If you're at all doubtful, follow your feelings. I'll stop them coming, and say you're not well.

Hamlet Certainly not. Forebodings indeed! God's love and care are infinite. What must be, will be: the readiness is all. Since we must go empty handed, what does it matter when we go? Don't fret.

[*The **King** and **Queen** come in with **Laertes**, **Lords**, **Osric** and **Attendants**, who bring swords and gloves and a table with wine and glasses on it*]

King Come, Hamlet, give him your hand!

Hamlet [*Shaking hands with **Laertes**] Forgive me, sir, for the wrong I have done you. As a gentleman, I'm sure you'll pardon me. Everyone here knows about the fearful illness that has afflicted me, and you too must have heard about it. It was not Hamlet who hurt your feelings, who insulted you, Laertes. It was his madness, and he himself was hurt by it. In front of all these people, I ask you to be generous enough to forgive me, since any harm I have done you was the result of thoughtlessness, not deliberate malice.

Laertes Your apology has certainly removed my strongest motive for revenge, but I must still demand a public reconciliation before my honour can be satisfied. For the moment, I accept your friendship in all sincerity.

Hamlet Good! Now we can go into the contest like brothers. But your skill will show up like fireworks against my dull performance!

Laertes You're making fun of me!

Hamlet No, I'm not.

King Osric, give them the weapons.

[*Osric offers **Hamlet** and **Laertes** swords*]

Laertes [*Taking one*] This is too heavy. Let me try another one.

Hamlet This suits me nicely. Are they all the same length?

Osric Yes, my lord. [*They get ready to fence*]

King [*To an **Attendant***] Pour out some wine. If Hamlet scores in the first or second round, I will drink to his health, and the cannon shall proclaim from the battlements that the King is drinking to Hamlet! Bring the glasses over here. [*The **Attendant** brings them*] Now begin! Judges, watch carefully!

[*They fence, and **Hamlet** hits **Laertes***]

Hamlet A hit!

Laertes No!

Hamlet What does the judge say?

Osric A hit, a clear hit!

Laertes All right! [*He prepares to fight again*] Come on!

King Wait! Let me drink. Hamlet, here's to your health! [*He drinks, the drum is beaten and a gun fires. Meanwhile the **King** puts poison in another glass of wine and hands it to an **Attendant***] Give this to Hamlet!

Hamlet No. I'll finish this round first. [*To **Laertes***] Come on! [*They fight, and **Hamlet** hits **Laertes** again*] Another hit!

Laertes Yes, it was. A touch.

King Our son will win.

Queen I'm afraid he's not very fit. [*To **Hamlet**, holding out her handkerchief*] Here, use *this!* [*He takes it and wipes his forehead. Meanwhile, the **Queen** takes the glass that has the poisoned wine in it*] I drink to you, Hamlet!

King Stop! Gertrude, don't!

Queen I will, my lord. Excuse me. [*She drinks, and then offers the glass to **Hamlet***]

King [*To himself*] Oh, my God! The poison—it's too late!

Hamlet I daren't drink just yet, madam. Later!

Laertes [*To the **King**, quietly*] Shall I hit him now, my lord?

King [*To **Laertes**, quietly*] I'm not sure that...

Laertes [*To himself*] I almost feel it's wrong...

Hamlet Come on, Laertes. You're not trying, you're playing with me.

Laertes You think so? Come on, then!

[*They fight, then stop*]

Osric Nothing!

Laertes Take that, then! [*He suddenly attacks **Hamlet** and wounds him. **Hamlet** gets angry and fights back in earnest. They both drop their swords, and in the confusion get hold of each others' swords. **Hamlet** then wounds **Laertes** with the poisoned sword*]

King Stop them! They're getting much too...

Hamlet [*To **Laertes***] Come on, come on!

[*The **Queen** collapses, poisoned*]

Osric [*To the **Attendants***] The Queen! Look after the Queen!

Horatio [*Looking at **Hamlet** and **Laertes***] They're both bleeding! [*To **Hamlet***] How are you, my lord?

Osric [*To **Laertes***] How are you?

Laertes Caught in my own trap, Osric. Killed by my own treachery!

Hamlet What's wrong with the Queen?

King It's the blood! It's made her faint!

Queen No! No! The drink! I've been poisoned, dear Hamlet! The drink! [*She dies*]

Hamlet Treachery! Lock the doors! Find out who's done this!

Laertes [*Falling to the ground*] He's here, Hamlet. And Hamlet, you're dead too. No medicine in the world can save you. You've only a few minutes to live; the treacherous weapon's in your hand, unprotected, poisoned. And I'm finished too: my crime has rebounded on me. Your mother's been poisoned. I can't... The King! The King's to blame...

Hamlet [*Looking at the sword*] The point—poisoned too! Then in you go! [*He stabs the **King** with it*]

Everyone Murder! Treason!

King Help me, friends! I'm only wounded...

Hamlet Here! you damned, murderous, incestuous Dane. Drink this! [*He forces the **King** to drink some of the poisoned wine*] Follow my mother! [*The **King** dies*]

Laertes He deserved it. He mixed the poison himself. Noble Hamlet, let us forgive each other! And may we both be forgiven for the deaths we have caused! [*He dies*]

Hamlet May heaven forgive you...! I am dying, Horatio. [*Looking at the **Queen***] Goodbye, poor unhappy woman! [*To everyone*] And all you, who have been silent witnesses to this fearful scene, if I had time, if death would stay his hand, I could tell you... But let it be. Horatio, I am dying, but you will live to tell the world the truth about me and explain why...

Horatio No! There is more of ancient Roman than Dane in me! There's still some poison left! [*He is about to drink the poisoned wine*]

Hamlet [*Pulling the glass out of* **Horatio's** *hand*] Let me have it! Let go! [*He empties the glass*] Oh Horatio, what will people think of me if you don't explain? For my sake, put up with this harsh world a little longer, and tell my story. [*Drums are heard in the distance*] What's that noise?

Osric It's young Fortinbras, signalling to the English ambassadors. He is back from his victory in Poland.

Hamlet The poison is getting the better of me, Horatio. I will never hear the news from England. But I see Fortinbras as the next King. He is my choice. Tell him what it is that— [*He dies*]

Horatio Good night, sweet Prince! May angels sing you to your rest! [*The sound of drums gets nearer*] Why are they marching here?

[**Fortinbras** *comes in with the* **English Ambassadors** *and some* **Attendants** *and* **Norwegian Soldiers**]

Fortinbras Where are they? [*He sees the dead bodies*] What a slaughterhouse! What butchery! What kind of infernal feast is Death planning here?

Ambassador A fearful sight! And we are too late to tell the King that his orders have been carried out, that Rosencrantz and Guildenstern are dead.

Horatio Oh, no! It was not the King who ordered their deaths. [*To Fortinbras*] Sir, since you have arrived so soon after this carnage, please give orders for the bodies to be put on public view, and allow me to tell the world how all this came about. You will hear of shameful, bloody and unnatural deeds, of chance and fate, of death by accident and by design, and of men caught in traps of their own making. I shall tell the whole truth.

Fortinbras We must act quickly, and summon the Court to hear it. As for me, I accept my good fortune with mixed feelings, but I do have a legitimate claim to this kingdom.

Horatio I'll have something to say about that as well, and I have a message from Hamlet which will gain you support. We must act immediately. With all this turmoil, delay could prove dangerous.

Fortinbras [*To an* **Officer**] Tell four officers to carry Hamlet in state to the castle wall. There is little doubt that he would have proved to be an excellent king. Beat the drums, to mark his passing! Remove the bodies: it's like a battlefield here! Order the guns to fire!

[*Drums beat as the bodies are carried out, then guns are fired*]

THE END